Forgotten Shipbuilders Of Belfast

WORKMAN, CLARK, 1880-1935

Laganside
Celebrating a Decade of Success

In 2004 Laganside Corporation celebrated the
10th Anniversary of the opening of the Lagan Weir

The Laganside Corporation celebrated a decade
of success in 2004. Although Laganside was
established by the government in 1989, it was
the opening of its first project, the revolutionary
Lagan Weir, in March 1994 that led to its
phenomenal success. It was the Lagan Weir
that breathed new life into the river and gave
Belfast a waterfront to be proud of.

Laganside started life as the 1987 Laganside
Concept Plan, which looked at ways of improving
the quality of the River Lagan and redeveloping
the land along its banks to bring about a much-
needed renaissance of a long-neglected area.
The 19th century and the coming of the Industrial

www.laganside.com

'Contributing to the revitalisation of Belfast and Northern Ireland by transforming Laganside to be attractive, accessible and sustainable, recognised as a place of opportunity for all.'

Revolution saw Belfast change from a small town to a major world-recognised port. Industries such as shipbuilding, linen, rope-making and tobacco blossomed, and throughout the city there was evidence of increased wealth and prosperity.

Sadly over the years Belfast turned its back on its river and the River Lagan became viewed as nothing more than an industrial thoroughfare with muddy polluted water, its riverbanks neglected and derelict. Laganside undertook a successful infrastructure led approach, which started with the building of the Lagan Weir, its aim being to maintain a minimum water level, covering the mudflats and creating an attractive reach of water.

The construction of the weir had a very positive impact on stimulating the regeneration process within Laganside's designated area. Today, Belfast has rediscovered its waterfront and the riverside has become a focus for business, leisure and cultural activity.

Laganside is now a centrepiece for business within Belfast and several national and international companies are located here, bearing testament to a shared confidence in the future economic performance of the city. By 2004 Laganside had secured 12,000 jobs in the area and over £800 million of investment, a figure which is expected to reach £1 billion by 2007.

Combined with the availability of high quality, stylish riverside and city centre apartments and a wealth of leisure activities to hand, the Laganside area is recognised as an ideal destination to live, work and play.

For further information please contact:
Laganside Corporation
Clarendon Building
15 Clarendon Road
Belfast BT1 3BG

Telephone 028 9032 8507
Email info@laganside.com

LAGANSIDE

This book contains a reprint of the following two volumes:

The shipbuilding & engineering works of
Workman, Clark&co., shipbuilders & engineers
First printed by Mc Caw Stevenson& Orr, Belfast, 1903

And

Shipbuilding at Belfast
First printed and published by J.Burrow,
London and Cheltenham, 1933
(original owned by the Linen Hall Library)

ISBN 0-946872-66-x

Copyright introduction John Lynch

Published this edition, 2004

Friar's Bush Press,
160 Ballylesson Road
Belfast BT8 8JU

Printer:
W&G Baird Limited
Caulside Drive
Antrim BT41 2RS

Forgotten Shipbuilders Of Belfast

WORKMAN, CLARK, 1880-1935

Introduction by John Lynch

FRIAR'S BUSH PRESS

Introduction

The premises of Workman, Clark and Co. were often described by the inhabitants of Belfast as the 'wee yard', but this was a joke, albeit a very Belfast joke! This shipyard could only be called the 'wee yard' in comparison with that of the other Belfast shipbuilder, Harland and Wolff. By 1895 Workman, Clark were the fourth largest British ship builder in terms of tonnage produced and employed 3,500 men.[1] Only in a shipbuilding district with two producers could Workman, Clark be considered 'wee', but throughout its history the firm was to be dwarfed by its neighbour. Indeed, the very survival of the other Belfast shipyard has resulted in the comparative obscurity of the activities of Frank Workman and George Clark. In the official history of Harland and Wolff there are twenty-four references to their rival, most of which are passing notes containing little information on the firm.[2] In fairness, however, when in 1933 Workman, Clark produced their *Shipbuilding at Belfast,* they managed to discuss this subject without mentioning the builders of the *Titanic.*

The story of Workman, Clark is one of the growth and commercial success of a major British shipbuilder, which can be contrasted with the company's eventual decline and closure as the world market changed. There is also a story of developing shipbuilding technology: the 'wee yard' may not have built the massive luxurious liners of their neighbour, but their ships enjoyed a fine reputation. Few records relating to the company have survived. Some say they were destroyed in the blitz, others that they were disposed of when the yard was 'sterilised'; the reconstruction of the firm's history can be seen as something of a historical detective story.

Origins of the firm

Francis, always known as Frank, Workman was born in Belfast on the 16th of February 1856, the youngest of fifteen children, including seven brothers, in the family of Robert and Jane Workman. The family had come to Belfast from Scotland in the early nineteenth century and were well-established muslin manufacturers. As the youngest son, Frank could not hope to enter the family business and received an education intended to allow him to make his own way in life. He attended the Royal Belfast Academical Institute until he reached the age of seventeen, in 1873, when he was enrolled as a premium apprentice at Harland and Wolff's yard.[3] Although David Johnson says it was only four years later that Frank established a four-acre shipyard on the north bank of the Lagan, most sources suggest this occurred in 1879, which seems more likely.[4] His former employers did not appreciate this, not least because Workman recruited another gifted individual from Harland and Wolff, William Campbell, to act as his yard manager. Although this might appear a foolhardy venture for such young men, even such gifted ones, Workman enjoyed potentially useful family links, notably by marriage into the Smith family of Glasgow, who owned the City Line.

Initially nothing was attempted beyond preparing the yard for business. Early in 1880, however, the company was joined by another individual George Clark, who was also linked to the Smith family, and at nineteen was even younger than his partner. He had been born in Paisley, to James Clark, a partner in a thread manufacturing firm, and Jane (née Smith) the daughter of the founder of the City Line. Educated at Merchiston Castle School in Edinburgh, he was apprenticed to Harland and Wolff in Belfast where he met Frank Workman.[5] The new partnership was registered in April 1880 and brought some badly needed working capital into the business; soon 150 men were at work on the firm's first orders, *Ethel* and *William Hinde.* The importance of family connections was demonstrated the following year when the yard received its first major order, from the City Line for the barque *City of Cambridge.* Family loyalty alone, however, was not sufficient to justify such orders, as this vessel was one of three sister ships ordered by the company from different yards, to allow comparison of performance and construction. The fact that subsequent work followed, including a 102-ton yacht for George Smith himself, would indicate that their relatives were satisfied with the young men's products.

In its early days the firm was desperately short of capital but the small size of the original yard, four acres, was not unusual, as contemporary shipbuilding firms often functioned on very limited sites. Belfast's third short-lived shipbuilding concern, McIllwaine and partners, had been established on a one-acre site and only expanded to four by 1880.[6] Likewise, the fact that for the first decade the engines were purchased from contractors was not uncommon, indeed Harland and Wolff also 'out sourced' engines in their early days and only established their engine works in 1879-80. Early Workman, Clark built ships had machinery produced by Rowan & Sons of Belfast, but subsequently a number of contractors were used before J & J Thompson of Glasgow became the main, but not exclusive, supplier.

Expansion in early stages
The yard slowly expanded in size, allowing ever larger and more complex vessels to be constructed, reaching fourteen acres by the end of the 1890s. Within two years of its opening the yard was constructing vessels of 400 foot length.[7] By 1891 it was decided that major capital investment in the form of an engine works was justified and Charles Allen joined the firm as engineering director with the task of establishing the new facilities. The new director was the son of the senior partner in the Allen Line who, on completing his apprenticeship with J&G Thompson of Clydebank, had joined his father's firm in their engineering department.[8] Workman, Clark were now proud to boast that they could undertake the complete construction of a ship and its machinery. Between 1880 and 1894 they built 114 vessels of all types, the largest of which was over five thousand tons. The firm had a fairly limited range of products. One apparent anachronism was the thirty sailing vessels produced in these years, notably after 1890 when a number of 2000 ton+ semi-sister ships were completed. These steel four masted ships were designed as low-cost bulk carriers for use in trades where speed was less important than cost. Over half the firm's production consisted of cargo ships (60 vessels) and, while a proportion were small craft for coastal or cross-channel work, a clear specalism in large ocean going types became discernable. Another type which featured in the building list (9 examples) was cargo-passenger vessels, which tended to be amongst the largest and more prestigious of the firms products in these years. In addition there were miscellaneous craft including harbour ferries and Dock Caissons (8 vessels) and a handful of barges and other small craft of various kinds. In their first year the firm launched only 7.2% of the tonnage of Harland and Wolff but this increased rapidly: in the first ten years they produced over 30% of Harland's tonnage and in 1894 Workman, Clark produced 50% of their rivals output.

The customer base of the company also expanded in these years, with a number of shipping lines becoming regular clients. Following the success of the *City of Cambridge* in 1882, the City Line ordered five large cargo vessels or passenger-cargo ships over the next decade and a total of eleven by 1901. In 1883, the company obtained its first order from the Head Line for the *Teelin Head*, notable for being the first ship built by Workman, Clark in steel, rather than iron, and for the fact that the owners, the Ulster S.S. Company, had previously been regular customers of Harland and Wolff. Only a few follow on orders came from this firm but, given their strong links to Harland and Wolff, even this could be seen as a success. Another local ship owner, who had previously used Harland and Wolff, was Corry's Star Line which, in 1886, ordered the *Star of Austria*. When Corry's began adding steamers to their fleet shortly afterwards, orders were placed with Workman, Clark establishing a relationship, which continued after Corry's amalgamated to form the Commonwealth and Dominion Line. In 1891 the Harrison Line of Liverpool ordered a cargo ship named *Wanderer*, the first of a dozen vessels for that customer.

Acquisition of MacIlwaine and Mc Coll yard
The completion, in 1892, of the cargo-passenger vessel *Southern Cross* proved that while Workman's yard could produce ships of the largest size, their facilities were becoming too cramped. These difficulties were overcome, in 1894, when they acquired the shipyard and engine works of the bankrupt firm of McIllwaine and McColl, on the south bank of the river. This acquisition increased the size of the firm's premises to forty acres with ten building slips, one of which was capable of taking a ship 700 feet long. The contemporary Belfast trades directory explained the dramatic effect of this acquisition,

> [Workman Clark] have also purchased the yard and engine works belonging to the firm of McIlwaine and McColl ltd. And thus have four separate establishments under their control....For the year 1893 they were 20th in the list of shipbuilders and for 1894 obtained sixth place. Thus demonstrating the great strides and growing importance of this young and enterprising firm[9]

Although there appeared to be duplication and overcapacity with two fully equipped engine works, the works in the original north yard manufactured engines and boilers for all vessels, while the southern works carried out repair work and produced auxiliary machinery, such as pumps and windlasses.[10]

Post-acquisition production
This increased capacity triggered a huge expansion in the firm's output in the next two decades and saw Workman, Clark emerge as a major British shipbuilder employing up to 5000 men by 1902.[11] The sailing ship finally vanished from the building list with the *Lord Dufferin* of 1896, as improved steamer design and better coaling facilities eroded the sailing vessel's limited advantages. In contrast, the firm

completed 111 cargo vessels between 1885 and 1914 and these became the most important product, significantly almost all of them being ocean-going craft rather than coasters. The passenger-cargo ship became increasingly important, with 43 of them being built in the two decades before World War One. Two new types of vessel began to be produced. In 1896-7 two passenger-cargo ships were completed, *Belvidere* and *Beverly;* with holds insulated with wooden cladding and additional ventilation fitted to allow them to transport of fruit. This system was adequate for vessels engaged in relatively local trade but for longer distances more effective technology was required and Workman, Clark claimed to have developed, between 1902 and 1904, a system whereby insulated cargo spaces were cooled by air ducted from refrigerated compartments. Before World War I Workman, Clark delivered 7 cargo vessels and 21 cargo-passenger craft, described as 'Fruiters' (16% of total output), and became leading producers of this type of vessel. The second development concerned the construction of substantial numbers of refrigerated vessels for transporting frozen meat from South America, Australia or New Zealand. These, unlike the 'fruiters', were simply listed as 'cargo' in the firm's advertising material but *Lloyd's Register* reveals that between 1892 and 1914 33 refrigerated cargo vessels and 16 passenger/cargo ships were delivered, 18% of the firm's output. In 1904 the firm completed the *Victorian* for J & A Allen, their first specialised passenger liner, to be followed by a dozen more before the war.

When the output of the 'wee yard' is compared to its neighbour the effects of this expansion become clear. In the first decade after the acquisition of the south yard, in 1894, Workman, Clark's production represented over 66% of Harland and Wolff's tonnage, and in 1901, for the first time, produced more tonnage than their rival. Between 1905 and 1913 Workman, Clark launched a hundred vessels whose tonnage was 83% of the seventy-one ships built by Harland and Wolff in Belfast, and they beat their neighbours output in 1909, 1910 and 1913. Employment in the yard also increased dramatically over these years from the 5000 'usually employed' in 1902 to 9000 in 1909 when they claimed the tonnage produced in the yard 'exceeded that of any other shipbuilding company in the United Kingdom'.[12] Of course by this stage Harland and Wolff were also building considerable numbers of vessels on the Clyde and therefore their total output was usually higher than the Belfast figure. As the number and average size of Workman, Clark ships being produced increased so too did their complexity. The firm's output in 1904 demonstrates how diverse and technologically advanced their production was. The *Victorian,* their first liner, was also the first merchant vessel powered by Parson's turbines, a development in which George Clark took a personal interest, and it was noted that both the ship and her engines were built by Workman Clark. The firm delivered the *Matatua*, a highly specialised frozen meat carrier, built for Shaw, Savill and Albion for the New Zealand trade and laid down the *Pacuare* and *Zent* for Elders & Fyffes West Indian Banana trade. Three other 'Fruiters' were supplied to United Fruit for the Caribbean/Latin

American trade. In the same year they delivered *H.M.S Squirrel*, a coast guard cruiser, the firm's only Admiralty order to date, and a new ferry, *No.6,* for the Belfast Harbour Commissioners.

The firm's customer base expanded after 1894 and a number of particularly significant shipping lines begin ordering vessels at about this time. In 1894 Alfred Holt and Co ordered *Sultan*, a cargo-passenger vessel, two large cargo carriers *Sarpedon* and *Hector* and the more modestly sized *Cerberus*. These orders were to be followed by 25 others making them Workman, Clark's largest customer. In the same year Houlder Line ordered *Urmston Grange* and were clearly happy with the vessel as they ordered seven more ships before 1901. Curiously it was not until Charles Allen had been with the firm for seven years that his father's company, Allen Line, ordered the passenger-cargo ship *Castilian* of 1898, although they ordered three more cargo/passenger ships and a liner before they were purchased by Ellerman Line, another well established Workman, Clark customer. United Fruit ordered their first three ships in 1904 and quickly became one of Workman, Clark's main customers, ordering 16 passenger/fruiter vessels, in batches of three or four, before the outbreak of war. Elders Fyffes, after ordering two fruiters in 1905, became another significant customer, ordering another five ships before the war. Lamport and Holt ordered two cargo vessels, delivered in 1900, followed by several other orders, the most significant of which were the three 'Vandyke' type liners, for their New York-South American services.

The greatest disappointment in these years was probably P&O, who ordered a pair of cargo vessels in 1903 and a passenger/cargo ship for delivery in 1905. There were, however, no other orders from this potentially valuable customer, who continued to have their ships built on the Clyde or by Harland and Wolff. This disappointment was balanced, to some degree, by orders from the Royal Mail Steam Packet Company for a cargo ship in 1904, and a liner in 1906. Although prestigious orders, nothing else was forthcoming from the RMSP Co. until a pair of cargo ships in 1913 and two cargo/passenger ships the following year.

Relations with Harland and Wolff

Relations between the Belfast shipbuilders have been presented as 'cool' if not positively antagonistic. The history of Harland and Wolff even suggests that there was considerable personal animosity between the principles of the two firms.[13] Two shipbuilders operating next door to each other would certainly be rivals and competitors, but there were important differences between them. Given their very different customer bases and specialisms, the two yards tended not to be in competition, except in exceptional circumstances. Indeed, even where they did seem to overlap this was largely superficial, as when Workman, Clark began building 'liners'. Their first ship of this type was the *Victorian,* which operated on the Liverpool to South America or the Canada routes. The P&O vessel *Araguaya* followed, designed for use on the firm's extensive far eastern routes; since the company were customers of Harland and Wolff this order might legitimately have been viewed as a case of 'poaching'. These ships were followed by two Orient Steam Navigation Company ships for use in the Australian emigrant service, followed by three *Anchiese* class ships for Alfred Holt and Co, for use on the same route. Holts ordered two larger vessels, delivered in 1912-3, to meet the growing demand for Australian passenger space. In the meantime, Workman, Clark had built the three *Vandykes* for Holt's New York-South America routes in 1911-12, 15-knot vessels, which represented a great improvement on previous ships. What emerges is a definite and quite distinctive pattern of construction. Workman, Clark was not building the high-speed leviathans in which Harland and Wolff specialised for the prestigious American routes, but rather smaller, slower ships for less glamorous trades.

As direct competition was reduced by different construction patterns, and because they needed to co-exist, the two shipyards co-operated on a day-to-day level. The Harland and Wolff papers show that communication between the two firms could be amicable or even friendly, notably during periods of industrial unrest or on questions of pay and employment conditions.[14] Although a degree of friction was inevitable, it was not in the interest of either company to allow this to get in the way of production or profits and indeed both seem to have accepted that collaboration was not only desirable but also necessary. It seems that mutual self-interest far outweighed antagonism between Belfast's shipbuilders in the late nineteenth and early twentieth centuries.

First World War

As with Harland and Wolff, and indeed every other shipbuilder who was not engaged in Admiralty work, the outbreak of the First World War caused serious difficulties for Workman, Clark, as resources were immediately diverted to naval construction. This initial disruption was short-lived and soon the firm was employing 12,000 men. They continued to build high quality merchant shipping, but in addition a certain amount of naval work was undertaken, although not enough to justify the claim made in the 1933 book that they had been 'solely engaged with Admiralty orders'. During the conflict a total of thirty-five vessels were built as 'Admiralty': 4 sloops, 7 patrol craft, 16 boom-defence vessels, 4 hospital vessels, two steam launches, a fast fleet tanker and a passenger-fruiter. In addition, two small monitors, designed for operations in coastal waters, were constructed on a sub-contract basis for Harland and Wolff, being launched and fitted out within eight weeks of the keels being laid.[15] Later in the war the yard began to construct standard merchant ships, under the direction of the Shipping Controller to replace the disastrous losses inflicted by German u-boats, although, as one writer noted rather snobbishly, these were 'built to government order on standards far below that of the yard'.[16]

It was not new construction, however, that formed the bulk of Workman, Clark's work during the war years, as the 1933 book points out, 'during that period 1,396 vessels were handled either for building [only 77 vessels naval and merchant were built] repairing or overhauling....the vessels dealt with approximated to one for every day of the war.' The first major naval work involved the conversion of four antiquated cruisers, of the *Edgar* class, into coastal bombardment vessels, for use off Flanders, which were completed in record time, by employing shifts of workers night and day.[17] The battle cruiser *Invincible* and the super-Dreadnought *Revenge* passed through the company's hands, as did semi-obsolete ships, of the *King Edward VII* and *Duncan* classes. Another ship overhauled by the firm, before her last voyage, was the armoured cruiser *Hampshire*, which was mined in June 1916 while on her way to Russia with Lord Kitchener on board. Other ships were fitted with anti-torpedo bilges known as blisters, which Workman, Clark claimed to have pioneered in the early cruiser conversions. They also claimed to have installed the first sets of paravane minesweeping equipment. Liners and cargo-liners were taken in hand for conversion to troop carriers, hospital ships, naval depot ships or auxiliary cruisers, often under conditions of extreme urgency. An example of how extensive such alterations could be was the conversion of a cargo ship into the destroyer depot ship *Sandhurst*. 'The fit-up for this purpose involved the erection on board of fitting shops, moulding shops, foundry, smithy and various other shops, so that repairs of any reasonable kind could be carried out on the destroyers without them having to return to port.'[18]

The firm responded rapidly to the demands of the war, as Belfast City Council's official history recorded,

'Some of these vessels have been turned out in very quick time. During their construction one of the firm's men established a new world's riveting record in the north yard, [John Moir drove 11,209 rivets in a normal working day on 5th June 1918] and the south yard and engine works replied by making a record in the way of finishing a standard ship, an 8,000 ton vessel being completed in 3 3/4 days from the time of launch.[19]

During these years the yard was extensively modernised and the number of construction berths was increased to 12, one of which, no. 8, could accommodate a hull of over 1000 feet. The firm, which had occupied about fifty acres in 1902, now had premises covering twice that area.

Sale of firm

After the war demand initially remained high, in 1920 Workman, Clark had orders for 37 ships and the labour force totalled 10,000.[20] On Thursday 23rd June 1921 in a special supplement to the *Belfast Newsletter*, published to celebrate the opening of the Northern Ireland Parliament, an article on Workman, Clark assured readers that,

This giant shipbuilding establishment has had a powerful influence on Ulster's industrial life, and year-by-year it is going forward to still greater success. In the new era which has dawned in the

Northern Province, with a Parliament fostering home industry, there are no limits to heights of success and expansion which Messrs Workman, Clark may yet reach, and the increased prosperity of the firm will be reflected in the lives of the people.[21]

The article went on to describe the growth and equipment of Workman, Clark's shipyard in glowing terms,

In order to complete this rapid summary of development, reference must be made to the fact that the company have recently completed a very large extension at their North Yard, bringing the area of their present premises up to 109 acres. On this extension new berths, capable of accommodating the largest and heaviest vessels, have been constructed and piled. The number of the building berths is now thirteen altogether, but, to allay the fears of the superstitious, it may be mentioned than an increase to that number is contemplated as soon as the present depression in trade shows signs of lifting. The company's works as they now stand are generally recognised as being among the most modern and complete in the world.

The concluding paragraph was clearly intended to display both commercial confidence and patriotic sentiment on that auspicious occasion,

In the building of high-class passenger and cargo steamers. Messrs Workman, Clark & Co. have a world-wide fame, and products of their skill are sailing on every sea. They have constructed many fine vessels for special trades, viz.: meat, fruit, cotton, timber, oil in bulk, grain and general cargoes. Space will not permit the mention of more than a few names ....are sufficient to show that the builders make no idle statement when claiming to be in the very forefront of this important section of the shipbuilding industry.
That the firm may go on in ever-increasing prosperity, bringing employment to thousands of people, and adding lustre to the reputation of the capital city of Northern Ireland is the sincere wish of every loyal Ulsterman.

Until this time control of the company remained in the hands of the Workman and Clark families. The founders were, however, in their sixties and, understandably, wanted to capitalise on their firm's success to safeguard their retirement. In late 1919 negotiations began with the Northumberland Shipping Company, in association with Sperling and Co, merchant bankers, for the purchase of a controlling interest.[22] Workman Clark's capital was increased to £2.4 million by the creation of 38 million new one-shilling shares. Frank Workman, whose Scottish nephew R.A. Workman was chairman of Northumberland Shipping, (a family connection that was later to prove highly embarrassing when accusations of malpractice were made), arranged the sale.[23] By January 1920, the purchasers had acquired sufficient shares to give them control and the share capital was again increased to £7 million by the issue of 1.6 million one-pound preference shares, with a guaranteed yield of ten per cent, plus 60 million one-shilling shares. Shortly afterwards a further £3 million of seven per cent stock was issued and a prospectus was published which claimed this cash would be used to develop the shipyard. In reality, however, most of the funds raised were redirected by the new board of directors to pay off an existing loan of

Northumberland Shipping. Workman expressed disquiet over the prospectus, but he eventually allowed himself to be overruled and both he and Clark remained on the board. Although clearly unhappy the former owners made a considerable profit as a result of this manoeuvre and subsequently, perhaps rather unjustly, were accused of being party to these dubious business activities.

As a consequence of these manoeuvres, the firm of Workman, Clark found itself saddled with a huge burden of fixed interest debt built up during a period of post-war boom. These debts made the company particularly vulnerable in financial terms to the coming depression. Over £4 million was involved in extremely complicated transactions, which saw large sums of money raised from share issues being invested in other companies,

£3,000,000 of seven per cent first-mortgage debenture stock was created, bought by Sperling & Company and offered for sale early in 1920 at 95 per cent. It was guaranteed as to principle, interest and premium by the Northumbrian Shipping Company and at the same time the new board sold realisable assets and reinvested the money in preference shares in the Northumberland Company, the purchase of John Watson Limited, colliery proprietors and 99 per cent of the capital of the Lanarkshire Steel Company.[24]

Finally, and probably too late to save their reputations, Frank Workman and George Clark resigned from the board in January 1921.

Depression and first bankruptcy

If the market for shipping had remained buoyant Workman, Clark might have been able to service this vast debt burden and survive as the firm was basically sound and its yards were modern and well equipped. A definite slump followed and by June 1921 orders had begun to dry up and recovery did not come quickly.[25] By 1925 the yard was only employing a quarter of their normal workforce, as against an average for the industry as a whole of 62%. The recently acquired burden of debt also created considerable problems and in 1923 the firm had to request a five-year moratorium on debt payments. By 1926 the company had made losses totalling over £3 millions and defaulted on its guarantee to meet interest payments on the debenture shares issued in 1920.

In 1927 a Belfast coachbuilder named William Urquhart, who had purchased a few of the income guaranteed shares, brought a court case against the Northumberland Shipping Co and a number of named individuals, claiming damages for deceit, conspiracy and statutory liability, based on the claim that the 1920 prospectus was misleading and fraudulent.[26] The case was complex and lengthy. Eventually the judge ruled out two of the allegations and ruled also that there was no evidence of malpractice by the directors of the pre-takeover company. The claimant finally accepted £130 as an out of court settlement, which encouraged other debenture holders to challenge the original trial judge's ruling in the Court of Appeal, where it was eventually reversed opening the way for further litigation. By this stage the death of Frank Workman had resulted in the withdrawal of accusations against him personally but the company was effectively left open to accusations of malpractice. In 1928 the shareholders succeeded in getting two joint receivers, R.J. Maskell and Hugh Smylie,[27] appointed and the company effectively closed down in January. The receivers invited tenders for the assets of the company, which consisted of equipment, plant and machinery, plus 1,241 fully paid ten-pound shares in the Cyclops Foundry and Pattern-making Company of Glasgow. While the bids were awaited, however, they also sought to raise money locally to recommence operations under new management.

Workman Clark (1928) Limited

The receivers hoped to persuade George Clark to resume control of the new company, on the grounds that he had been less directly implicated than other directors in the take-over and enjoyed a good reputation, but he declined, on health grounds. Attempts to find a new managing director finally succeeded when William Strachan, who had been Workman, Clark's company secretary for twenty-four years, agreed to become chairman of a new limited company. The new company, rather originally named Workman Clark (1928) Ltd, began operations in March 1928 with government support provided under the Loans Guarantee Act. They tried, at least in advertising material, to present recent events in a positive light:

> This year, 1920, saw the business pass from its founders into other hands; but old associations were maintained while new connections were established. The subsequent industrial depression struck the business a heavy, but not fatal, blow. Like its own good ships, it weathered the storm although it had to turn into port for re-fitting. This took the form of a re-organisation of the Company's affairs, and in March, 1928, it set forth again as Workman Clark (1928) Limited.

Although this gives a romantic, if not heroic, view of the foundation of the new company, Strachan and his colleagues faced serious problems, not the least of which was a shortage of orders due to the closure of yard in early 1928. The only customer was Belfast City Council who ordered the 360-ton sludge vessel Divis. Equally worrying was continuing litigation over debentures; only when the shareholders finally agreed to accept £33 6s 8d for every £100 of stock held, was the new company freed from its predecessor's debts. Despite these problems there remained a deep-seated belief that the slump in shipbuilding was temporary and that prosperity would inevitably return.

These years also saw the collapse of many customer relationships that had sustained Workman's before the war and new orders proved increasingly difficult to attract. It is perhaps symptomatic that the first major orders the new firm received, the Agamemnon for Holt's Blue Funnel Line and City of Sydney for Ellerman, both came from long established customers, who never subsequently ordered another

vessel. At the time, however, this was not known and there was an air of optimism in April 1929;

> The Agamemnon was specially welcome, as Messrs Alfred Holt & Co. had been one of the best customers of the old Workman, Clark firm and as it represented the first big contract secured by the new firm. Interest in the Deebank lay in the fact that she was the first vessel launched from the south yard under the new regime at Workman, Clark's and was the first contribution by that firm to the fleets controlled by Andrew Weir & Co.[28]

Wall Street and Bermuda fire

There could not have been a worse moment to attempt to revive a shipbuilding firm, although this can, perhaps, only be seen with hindsight. The yard had only just returned to something akin to pre-war production levels when, on 29th October 1929, the American stock market crashed. The collapse of the world's most prosperous economy was bound to have serious effects on world trade and inevitably less trade meant less demand for shipping. This was made worse by the fact that the world's merchant fleets, as a result of war losses and emergency building programmes, was largely composed of comparatively new vessels and there was little demand for replacements.

The prosperity of Belfast's shipyards vanished and Workman, Clark were pitifully ill prepared for the troubled times ahead. By the end of 1930 Strachen was proposing that Workman, Clark and Harland and Wolff combine,[29] a suggestion rejected by H&W who were also facing serious difficulties. On November 28th 1930 Workman, Clark announced that were closing their shipyard for a period 'not exceeding' two months from the 20th of December and their engine works for a month.[30] The firm desperately sought new customers and tried to develop new areas of production such as the whaling factory ships, designed for open-sea operations, built for Norwegian owners, 17,800-ton Kosmos of 1929 and the 16,966-ton Kosmos II of 1931. These ships were technically successful but hopes of further orders were frustrated by a slump in the whaling industry in the early 1930s. In May 1932, following the completion of the fruit carrier Erin, the yard had no work on hand and no orders. Addressing a large party of invited guests on board the Erin after her trials Strachan admitted 'all our slips are empty' but added 'but we are neither downhearted or without hope'.[31] By December the press was full of still more dismal news and it was reported that 90% of the labour force were idle.[32]

It was not only the lack of new orders that depressed the management of Workman, Clark. Just before the launch of the Erin the company were forced to purchase from an owner a vessel which had suffered serious damage while in their hands for repair. The 20,000-ton motor liner Bermuda was built by Workman, Clark for Furness Withy & Co in 1927 for use on their New York-Bermuda route and as a cruise liner. As the largest and most luxurious vessel built by the firm, she was a source of considerable pride, being used in the firm's advertising material, but she became something of a white elephant for her owners after the Wall Street Crash. On the 17th of June 1931 the ship was seriously damaged by fire and, following temporary repairs, she was returned to her builders for what amounted to reconstruction.[33] In November a second fire occurred while the ship was in Workman, Clark's hands and the vessel effectively burnt out; early in May 1932 the owners issued a writ claiming damages of almost a million pounds.[34] To settle the case Strachan and his colleagues agreed to purchase the burnt out hulk.

Final decline

In 1933 Workman, Clark issued their book *Shipbuilding in Belfast* as an advertising measure intended to attract new orders. Although the shipping industry remained depressed the firm did receive some important orders. In 1933 Andrew Weir ordered three moderately sized motor passenger ships with refrigerated cargo holds and Federal Liners two large refrigerated cargo carriers, but when these ships were delivered no new orders arrived from these companies to fill the yards slips. In 1934 the last order was received from the Anglo-Saxon Oil Company for an 8,000-ton tanker named *Acavus* and by December the *Belfast Telegraph* was reporting bad news to its readers 'The work obtained in 1932 and 1933 has been completed, but inquiries for further tonnage are being constantly pursued so that the present spell of depression may be brought to an end.'[35] There was nothing but repair work to keep the yard in operation although some of these contracts were significant, such as the instillation of electro-turbo engines in six vessels of the Ellerman Line in 1933-4.

By the beginning of 1935 the labour force was placed on a day-to-day basis and slowly the skilled labour that was critical to the yard's survival drained away, not a few going to H&W. It was increasingly recognised that the firm was doomed and that closure was inevitable. At the end of February 1935 most of the office staff were given a month's notice and on March 13th, in the Northern Ireland Parliament, it was suggested for the first time that National Shipbuilders Security were interested in the firm.[36] This syndicate had been established in 1930 by 46 shipbuilders, including Harland and Wolff and Workman, Clark, with a capital of £1,000,000 to purchase and dismantle redundant shipyards and so reduce excess capacity in the industry. After a further period of uncertainty, on 20th April 1935 it was announced that the yard was to be sold and closed.[37]

The *Belfast Telegraph* report noted that 'many of the men formally employed by Workman, Clark have already found work on the Island [Harland & Wolff] which has also been able in recent months to take over most of the draughtsmen and tracers and apprentices to the different trades'.[38] It was not only human assets, however, that were stripped from the stricken firm, it was noted that Harland and Wolff were interested in acquiring Workman Clark's south yard which was adjacent to their own. The matter was discussed at the Annual Meeting of Harland and Wolff's shareholders in May[39] and a deal was made which allowed Harland and Wolff to acquire the yard,

in return for closing a yard on the Clyde.[40] Certainly, according to contemporary newspaper reports, Harland and Wolff must have been more interested in the land than the facilities of the south yard which appears to have been almost derelict by 1935.[41] The north yard was closed and its plant and equipment auctioned off on 4th September 1935 as the *Irish News* reported,

> Men who had been employees of the 'Wee Yard' some of them for over 40 years, watched while the hammers of the auctioneers marked the sale of machines which they had operated for mayhap half their lifetime, and on whose operation depended their livelihood. Most of them are now engaged in a temporary capacity dismantling those very machines whose ever mood they knew and loved, and knowing at the same time that every bolt they turned, every girder they carried away, brought them nearer the day when they should forsake the yard forever.[42]

The terms of the purchase stated that the site could never again be used for shipbuilding. A number of suggestions were made for alternative uses, including a suggestion that an aircraft factory might be established,[43] and a proposal in December 1937 to establish a ship-breaking yard site, which was sufficiently attractive to ensure an offer of government assistance, under the New Industries Development Act.[44] However, this latter project failed to develop and, fourteen months after closure, the Harbour Commissioners auctioned off the final remnants of the yard to clear the site in 1939,

> The skeletons of buildings where once thousands of skilled Belfast craftsmen worked in connection with the construction of such well-known vessels as the Voltaire and the Vandyck and hundreds of others are practically all that now remain of Messrs Workman Clark's famous North Yard, and soon they will be razed to the ground. Memories of the yard were conjured up at the at the auction to-day of buildings which had been demolished or were in the process of demolition.[45]

With the outbreak of World War Two there were suggestions that the North Yard should be reopened,[46] but by now the site was in such a condition that this would have proved impossible. The Lagan Construction Company, which built a number of landing craft, occupied the site during the war years but after that it was finally abandoned for shipbuilding.

Conclusion

Although shipbuilding in Belfast has tended to become associated with Harland and Wolff, the story of Workman, Clark deserves to be remembered. The 'wee yard' was a major British shipbuilder employing thousands of men and producing high quality ships of the most advanced type. The two books reprinted in this volume allow an insight into this lost firm and hopefully give the reader a sense of the intense pride felt by those who worked in the yards.

References

1   *Belfast trades directory* (1896) Introduction
2   Moss, M. & Hume J.R., *Shipbuilders to the world* (Belfast, 1986)
3   David Johnson, 'Francis Workman' *Dictionary of Business Biography*
4   Bowden, F.C., 'Shipbuilders of other days: no 36 Workman, Clark and Co' *Shipbuilding and Shipping Record* Dec. 29 1949, p. 785
5   David Johnson, 'Clark, Sir George Smith' *Dictionary of Business Biography*
6   Lynch J.P. 'Belfast's third Shipyard' *Ulster Folklife* Vol. 41 (1995).
7   *Belfast Newsletter*, 23 June 1921
8   Bowden, *Shipbuilders*, p. 785
9   *Belfast trade directory* (1894)
10 Bowden, *Shipbuilders*, p. 786
11 *Belfast trade directory* (1904)
12 *Belfast trade directory* (1914)
13 *Shipbuilders to the world*, p.43
14 Lynch J.P., *An unlikely success story* (Belfast,2001), p. 17
15 Moss & Hume, *Shipbuilders to the world* p.181
16 Bowden, Shipbuilders, p. 786
17 Belfast City Council, The Great War 1914-18 (Belfast, 1919), p.120
18 ibid p. 122-3
19 ibid p. 122
20 Johnson 'Clark'
21 *Belfast Newsletter,* 26 June 1921
22 Bowden, *Shipbuilding,* p.788
23 Johnson 'Workman'
24 Bowden, *Shipbuilding* , p. 788
25 *Belfast Newsletter,* 26 June 1921
26 *Belfast Newsletter,* 28 October 1927
27 *The Northern Whig,* 2 March 1928
28 *Belfast Telegraph,* 25 April 1929
29 Moss & Hume, *Shipbuilders to the world,* p. 288
30 *Belfast Telegraph,* 28 November 1930
31 *The Northern Whig,* May 30 1932
32 *Belfast Telegraph,* 20 December 1932
33 *The Irish News,* 3 May 1932
34 *Irish News,* 3 May 1932
35 *Belfast Telegraph,* 20 December 1934

36 *Belfast Telegraph,* 13 March 1935.
37 *Belfast Telegraph,* 20 April 1935
38 Ibid.
39 The *Northern Whig,* May 3 1935
40 Moss & Hume, *Shipbuilders to the world* , p. 307
41 *Belfast Telegraph,* 22 April 1935
42 *Irish News,* reprinted as 'on this day September 4 1935', 4/9/2004
43 *Belfast Newsletter,* 22 April 1935
    Northern Whig, 3 May 1935
    *Belfast Telegraph,*14 May 1935
44 *Belfast Newsletter,* 16 December 1937
45 *Belfast Telegraph,* 2 February 1939
46 *Belfast Telegraph,* 28 March 1940

THE
SHIPBUILDING & ENGINEERING WORKS
OF

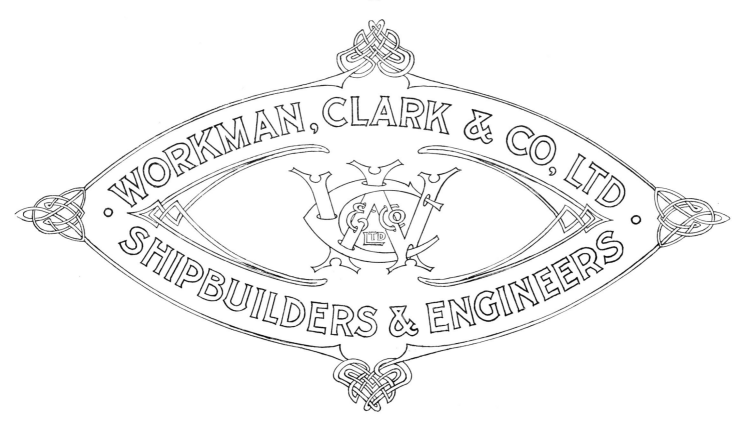

WORKMAN, CLARK & CO, LTD

SHIPBUILDERS & ENGINEERS

BELFAST, IRELAND.

First Printed In 1903

Introductory.

THE great revolution in commercial methods, which forms one of the outstanding features of the last century's history, was in the main a silent one. The processes which made for greater efficiency and economy were not based upon any rigid plan, but were adopted as ever-changing conditions made departures from old-fashioned methods essential, and in no branch of our industrial life have greater changes taken place than in the building of ships. In order to maintain our commercial supremacy, and retain our hold of the largest share in the oversea carrying trade of the world, it was necessary for the shipbuilder to meet the altered conditions thrust upon us by the competition of foreign rivals, who in many instances relied upon State aid to further their endeavours. For this purpose we now build the largest ships, and introduce specialization into every one of the complex departments of our modern yards.

Workman, Clark & Co., Ltd., have one of the best equipped concerns in the United Kingdom, and the situation occupied by their works is admirably suited for shipbuilding operations. The firm has built vessels for the principal steamship lines of to-day, and each succeeding year sees an increase in the tonnage turned out.

The River Lagan, of which Belfast Lough forms the estuary, is remarkably well adapted for such work; and the two yards owned by the Company command the broadest and deepest part of the river. The demand for ships of great carrying capacity and strength has led to the introduction of hydraulic and electrically driven machinery; and in these yards there are complete installations of labour-saving plant, by means of which heavy work is expeditiously turned out. From the reception of an order for a steamer until she is handed over to the owners, every item in her construction is made by Workman, Clark & Co., Ltd.: she is engined by them, fitted out with auxiliary machinery of all kinds, and internally completed for either the passenger or the cargo trade; and the vessels built by them are familiar in every important port in the world.

Having said so much introductory to a general survey of the yards, engine works, repairing department, and other important sections, we come to a more particular enumeration of their special features.

PANORAMIC VIEW SHEWING THE POS

OF THE WORKS OF THE COMPANY.

GENERAL VIEW OF NORTH YARD.

END VIEW OF DRAWING OFFICE.

THE NORTH YARD.

A superficial glance over the North Yard shows the outstanding features of the arrangement to be the size and height of the various workshops. These are constructed of corrugated iron, and fitted with the most modern plant and machinery, driven by steam, electricity, and hydraulic power, and the various installations are complete and self-contained. The fitting-out wharf, which flanks the western side of the yard, also demands attention.

THE ADMINISTRATIVE BLOCK.

The Administrative Buildings, situated at the entrance, constitute what may be described as the centre of the industrial life of the concern. Taking the various departments seriatim, the commercial offices consist of a suite of admirably designed and substantially constructed buildings, the heads of the firm being accommodated in self-contained suites, while the managers' consulting rooms are in close proximity to those of the principals, and from this point there is communication by telephone to departmental managers and superintendents. Looking out on the rear, a large fireproof building is observed, and here are kept plans, calculations, books of the firm, and other important documents.

THE DRAWING OFFICE.

The Drawing Office is one of the most important of the various departments which make up the yard as a whole. In it are designed the vessels which are so well known to travellers to all parts of the world; and being really the fountain-head of all the complex details of shipbuilding, it follows, as a matter of course, that the greatest care has been taken with its construction and equipment. It is well lighted, and, like the other offices, is heated at an equable temperature all the year round. A large staff of competent draughtsmen is engaged, who execute their work under the most favourable conditions. This building has been recently extended and improved, bringing it into line with the requirements of a continuously developing business, which makes increased demand upon the drawing staff.

INSIDE THE NORTH YARD, LOOKING EAST.

A PORTION OF THE COUNTING HOUSE.

THE MOULDING LOFT.

THE RIGGERS' SHED.

10

MOULDING LOFT AND RIGGERS' SHED.

At the Moulding Loft, which is upwards of 200 feet in length by 70 feet wide, is reached one of the first stages in the process of shipbuilding. In this spacious and well-lighted building the plans from the Drawing Office are transferred to the practical department of actual work. Underneath is the Riggers' Shed, identical in length with the Moulding Loft, and here is kept a varied assortment of wire hawsers, machinery for serving wire, blocks, and gear of every kind for lifting heavy weights.

The Model-makers' Shop is a most interesting place, in which important work is done, each vessel having to be modelled exactly to scale before the actual construction is commenced.

THE PAINT SHOP.

The Paint Shop is designed and built to accommodate a large stock of paints and varnishes. Having regard to the inflammable nature of materials stored, elaborate precautions are taken to guard against fire. For this purpose, modern appliances to cope with any outbreak are provided throughout the yard, and members of the City Brigade are constantly on duty and in direct communication with the Central Station.

TIMBER STORAGE.

Crossing the main road, which intersects the yard, the Timber Storage area is reached. This occupies about five acres, which are utilized to their fullest extent. The deck planks, etc., are stored under cover in perforated drying sheds, through which the wind has free course to do its preservative work, and here are also kept the expensive and beautiful woods used in saloon fittings and in the decorative work which now constitutes such a pleasing feature of cabin, drawing-room, smoke-room, and other portions of the ship set apart for the use of passengers. The Cabinetmakers' and Joiners' Shops are in close proximity, and the materials are so disposed as to be available to the tradesmen with the least possible delay.

A CORNER OF THE MODEL SHOP.

PART OF THE TIMBER YARD.

EXTERNAL VIEW OF NORTH YARD AND FITTING-OUT BASIN.

FITTING-OUT BASIN, WITH CITY AND P. & O. LINERS ALONGSIDE.

A CITY LINER IN THE FITTING-OUT BASIN.

THE JOINERS' SHOP.

Still dealing with wood-work fittings, the Joiners' Shop claim attention. This is a building measuring about 200 feet by 130 feet and running parallel with the finishing jetty, so that interior furnishings can be easily transferred to the ships in the basin. Each floor of the shop is replete with the latest machinery for turning out the best fittings and cabinet work; and close upon 300 joiners benches are in constant use. All the machinery in use here is electrically driven, and the most modern labour-saving devices are fully utilized. Parenthetical reference may be made to the large polishing and patternmakers' shops, and to the foremen's offices in the centre of the yard, since these closely adjoin the shop under notice.

IN THE FITTERS' SHOP.

BASEMENT.

THE JOINER SHOP.

THE FITTERS' SHOP.

The Fitters' Shop is an important department, fitted with powerful lathes, boring and planing machines, drills and other tools. Fittings used on the hull of the ship, such as those in connection with winch piping, steering gear, steam heating, etc., are made here, and the upkeep and repair of the yard machinery also receives attention.

FITTING-OUT BASIN.

The next item in connection with the north yard which calls for description is the Fitting-out Basin, which is conveniently situated on its western side. The basin is about 1,000 feet long by 200 feet wide, and within recent years deepening operations have been completed, assuring an ample draught of water at all states of the tide. The wharf covers a large area, and is substantially built, in order to sustain the weight of the heavy cranes and other machinery used in fitting-out work.

THE MAIN PLATERS' SHED.

14

CARPENTERING AND SPAR WORK.

Although steel-built ships exclusively are turned out by the firm, there is of necessity a considerable amount of wood-work required. For this reason the Carpenters' Shop is an important part of the establishment, and a large number of hands is employed. The Spar Shed, where wooden masts, spars, teak seatings, etc., are made, adjoins the Carpenters' Shop.

INTERNAL STRUCTURE OF A VESSEL.

ONE OF THE FURNACES.

SPAR SHED.

THE POWER STATION.

The Power Station occupies a central position, within easy reach of the electrically-driven machinery, and from here current for lighting purposes is transmitted. Two marine engines of modern type, and constructed by the firm, are in operation : one driving the generator, which supplies the power for the plating machinery motors; while the other furnishes current for illuminating purposes. There are also five large multi-tubular boilers, which supply steam for the above machinery, and also for general use throughout the yard.

PLATING.

Coming to the Platers' Shed, this is furnished with two large frame boards, each about 70 feet square, and brief reference may be made to the work which is done here. The frames of the ship are drawn full size upon the boards, and after the sets have been made they are transferred to blocks alongside the furnace. The steel bars are furnaced and set on the blocks to their respective shapes, as taken from the frame board. After being set, the bars are taken back to the frame boards, tried, and corrected if necessary. They are then marked and conveyed to the punching machines, and subsequently screwed up in readiness for the hydraulic riveters.

Leaving this shed and proceeding in the direction of the most southerly slip, another extensive Platers' Shed is reached, in which the mechanical appliances are practically similar to those already described. The shed contains several powerful punching and planing machines, and rollers for flattening steel plates. One set of rolls is over 30 feet in length, and is capable of rolling and bending cold plates $1\frac{1}{2}$ inches thick ; the top roller, which weighs about 40 tons, working over two rollers of smaller diameter.

THE PLATERS' SHED.

TWO SIDE BAYS.

16

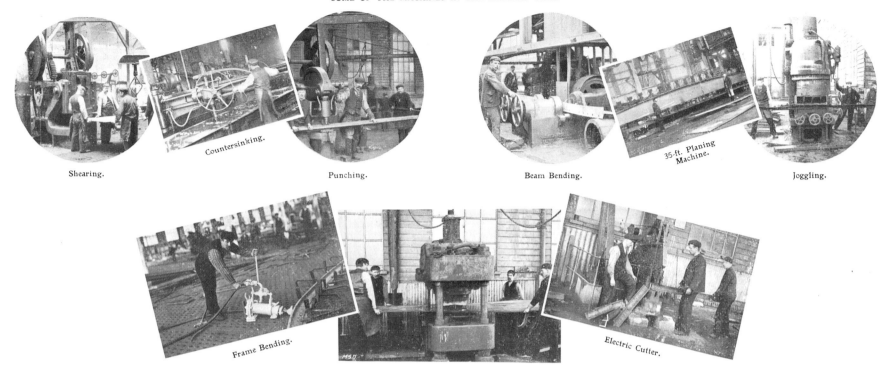

Shearing.   Countersinking.   Punching.   Beam Bending.   35-ft. Planing Machine.   Joggling.

Frame Bending.   Manhole Punching.   Electric Cutter.

THE FURNACES, &c.

In the Platers' Shed are situated the plate and frame furnaces, the former being capable of heating plates 30 × 7 feet. The furnaces are heated by gas, and a light railway system throughout the building carries the plates and bars to the desired machine. Close to the furnaces is a large bevelling machine; and as the frame bars come out of the furnace they are bevelled to the required angles. By means of this machine heavy and difficult manual labour is saved, and markedly superior work turned out. Two large hydraulic machines—one for punching manholes in plates, and the other for joggling—save much time and ensure a better quality of workmanship. The frame joggling machine is perhaps the more important of the two, since by its introduction the use of packing and liners have been done away with, thus saving considerable weight, and achieving the important desideratum of enabling a ship to carry more cargo. A large four-sided punching and shearing machine finishes off the plates in one spot; and amongst other auxiliary items is a shearing machine capable of cutting the heaviest sections of angle bars, tees, channels, Zed and H bars. Electricity supplies the motive power in each of the above cases.

FITTING AND BEAM BENDING.

Forming what may be described as an annexe to the plating department, is the general fitting shed, in which are several large punching machines, for use on the heaviest plates. In the beam shed, beams are prepared for the ships by two sets of benders, one of which is capable of bending cold the weightiest built T beams, and there is also an electrically-driven punching machine and an angle iron shearing machine, as well as a hydraulic power angle iron cutting machine, designed to cut the largest sections of beams rolled. Alongside these machines are the beam skids; and as the men at the bending machines complete their part of the work, the beams are riveted hydraulically on the skids. Then the locomotive cranes come along, pick up the beams, and transport them to the vessels, two men being sufficient to cope with this very heavy work.

ON THE CENTRE LONGITUDINAL.

ON THE KEEL PLATE.

THE HYDRAULIC RIVETER AT WORK.

18

HYDRAULIC RIVETING.

At this stage it may be mentioned that there are few yards in which so much hydraulic riveting is executed as in the yard under notice. All the heavy keel riveting and several strakes of the adjacent shell plating are so treated, as well as the sheerstrake and entire interior of the double bottom. In addition to the practical utility and speed of the hydraulic process, it should be remembered that however skilled workmen may be, they cannot cope satisfactorily or adequately with the heavy labour involved in hand riveting on the large steamers turned out in these yards. The work on the sheerstrake, for instance, is so laborious that it taxes their strength to the utmost, and it is therefore absolutely necessary that another method should be adopted. It is satisfactory to state that the hydraulic riveting in all parts of the ship has been found to meet every requirement, and the steamers are launched as staunch and sound as steel plates can be joined together.

THE FRAME BLOCKS.

SMITHS' SHOP.

Before passing from this part of the yard, the large smithy demands attention. Here forty blacksmiths' fires are kept constantly going, and there is a complete installation of modern labour-saving machinery and appliances. Eight steam hammers of powerful type are in operation, while there are numerous others of graduated power. Jib cranes, attached to which are hydraulic lifts capable of raising the heaviest forgings, are fitted throughout the building, and large fans, driven by electric motors, supply blast to the fires.

IN THE SMITHY.

19

BOW VIEW.   STERN VIEW.

ONE OF THE BUILDING SLIPS, SHEWING P. & O. LINER ON THE STOCKS.

LAUNCH FROM NORTH YARD.

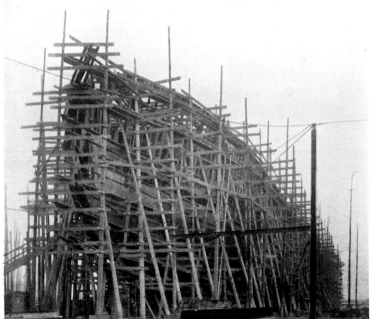

VIEW OF VESSEL IN FRAME.

BUILDING BERTHS.

Crossing over a maze of railway and trolley rails of various gauges radiating throughout the yard, one comes to the building slips. These are five in number, situated on ground which has been heavily piled, in order to afford the requisite stability indispensable in building ships of great cargo-carrying capacity. Alongside each slip are placed large derricks about 120 feet in height, which serve to lift heavy weights aboard the steamers when in course of construction. The old system of launching vessels has been superseded by the hydraulic trigger system.

GENERAL VIEW OF SOUTH YARD.

SOUTH YARD BUILDING SLIPS, FROM THE RIVER

THE SOUTH YARD.

Much of the space occupied by this yard is land which has been reclaimed from the sea, the rapid development of the business of the firm making it imperative that increased facilities should be provided for the building of ships. Very considerable sums of money have been expended in perfecting this yard, and it will bear comparison with any in the United Kingdom.

The description already given in detail of the various departments in the north yard will apply more or less accurately to the sections into which the south yard is divided. There are sheds for platers, frame setters, angle-iron smiths, blacksmiths, fitters, joiners, painters, riggers, riveters, etc., and in all important details the operations are similar to those described in the opening pages of this volume.

IN THE SOUTH YARD PLATING SHED.

THE BUILDING SLIPS.

Entering the yard from the river side, the Building Slips first demand attention. Four of these have been laid down, each of which is capable of dealing with the largest vessels, and there is room for a fifth, which will be made in the not distant future. At the east side of the yard, where the launches take place, there is a deep and broad fairway, flanked on the south by the fitting-out wharves, alongside of which vessels are laid for completion or repairs. A broad-gauge railway runs through the yard, connecting it with local systems, and there is a complete narrow-gauge line connecting each of the shops with the slips.

SOUTH YARD JOINERS' SHOP.

LAUNCH FROM SOUTH YARD.

PLACING BOILERS ON BOARD A HOULDER LINER AT THE 100-TON CRANE.

24

THE SAWMILL.

The Sawmill is one of the most interesting buildings on this side of the river. It is purely self-contained, every operation in connection with the cutting of timber being performed by means of modern machinery. The unloading jetty is connected with the mill by rail, and when the cranes pick up the logs they are run on trucks to the saws, where they are quickly cut into the scantlings required for decks, etc. They are next racked and dried on the hot-air system, and eventually take their place in the ship in such a perfect condition as to give the most satisfactory results in regard to durability.

REPAIR WORK.

The outfitting and repairing staff is housed in new and commodious sheds and shops in immediate proximity to the fitting-out wharves and to the Alexandra Graving Dock. This dock has an overall length of 820 feet, and an extreme breadth of 92 feet; but a contract has just been completed by the Harbour Commissioners for another and larger dock, which, when finished, will be the finest of its kind in the world. Besides these, there are in the port several other docks of smaller dimensions; one of them, the Hamilton Graving Dock, being capable of accommodating vessels up to 450 feet long. Thus every facility is enjoyed for the rapid disposal of repair work, now an important feature in the operations of the firm; Government and private contracts alike being dealt with. In the Repairing Shops, the stores comprise everything necessary for refitting vessels; and here the steel masts, cranes, and ventilators are made for both yards. On the jetty is situated a powerful steam crane, with a lifting capacity of 100 tons, and alongside the crane there is a depth of water equal to ships of any tonnage.

THE ALEXANDRA GRAVING DOCK, SHEWING TWO OF H.M. FIRST-CLA

26

UISERS IN THE DOCK FOR REPAIR AT THE SAME TIME.

EXTERIOR OF ENGINE AND BOILER WORKS.

FOUR BAYS   IN ENGINE SHOP.

INTERIOR OF ENGINE SHOP.

BOILERS IN COURSE OF ERECTION IN THE BOILER SHOP.

30

ENGINE AND BOILER WORKS.

The Engine and Boiler Works consist of turning, fitting, and erecting shops, smithy and forge, pattern shop, power house, and boiler shops, together with the numerous stores and offices, these all being on one level, but in separate, well-ventilated buildings, with ample head-room for the construction of the largest marine engines and boilers. Special attention has been given to crane power, and a complete installation of overhead cranes has been fitted, capable of dealing with the heaviest class of work. The buildings are constructed of corrugated iron, and in appearance externally are of massive proportions; the engine shop, for instance, having a total clear height from floor to ceiling of 75 feet.

The machinery throughout is of the most modern type, adapted for the manufacture of all classes of marine engines, both reciprocating and turbine, and arranged for efficiently and economically turning out the work; the boiler shops also being thoroughly equipped with a complete up-to-date hydraulic and pneumatic plant.

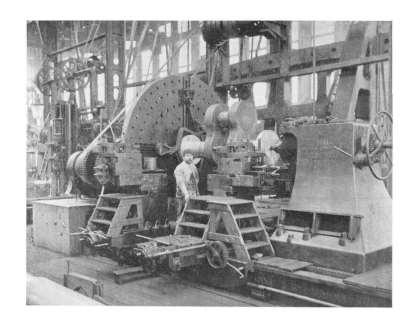

IN THE ENGINE SHOP.

THE ENGINE WORKS POWER HOUSE.

32

The whole works are driven and lighted electrically from the central power house in the Engine Works, where the generating plant is placed. This plant consists of a large dynamo, which is driven direct by a set of triple expansion marine type of engines, of over 1,000 I.H.P., constructed in the works by the firm, also a smaller dynamo for night work, driven by horizontal compound engines.

ABERCORN WORKS.

A short distance from the main engine works are situated the Abercorn Engine and Boiler Repair Works. These works are within a few yards of the 60-ton sheer-legs and the Hamilton Graving Dock, the latter, as already stated, being capable of accommodating vessels up to 450 feet long, and are also within easy access of the Alexandra Graving Dock and 100-ton crane. They have been thoroughly equipped with the latest tools and appliances for dealing with all classes of repairs, and in addition to repair work, the various auxiliaries for the main engine works are constructed here, including steam winches, steering gears, turning engines, reversing engines, centrifugal circulating pumps, etc., etc.; the aim of the Company being to furnish their ships, as far as possible, with auxiliaries of their own special design and manufacture.

COLD BENDING MACHINE IN BOILER SHOP.

STEAM WINCH.

PUMPING ENGINE.

STEERING GEAR.

In the following pages will be found a list of the shipowners for whom Workman, Clark & Co., Ltd., have built vessels, with illustrations of a number of these vessels; also a short descriptive account of the first Transatlantic turbine steamer, "Victorian," at present being built and engined at their works.

A glance at the following list will shew the varied class of work which has been turned out by this firm.

First-class Transatlantic Mail Steamers up to 550 feet long.

Cross Channel Passenger Steamers.

Cargo Liners up to 20,000 tons displacement.

Insulated Meat-Carrying Steamers up to 600,000 cubic feet capacity.

Fruit-Carrying Steamers.

Full-rigged Sailing Ships and Barques.

Caissons for Dock Entrances.

Steam Ferries.

Lighters and Launches for Transhipment abroad.

Paddle Steamers for Excursion Traffic.

Steam and Sailing Yachts.

THE TONNAGE RETURNS for the year 1902 shew Workman, Clark & Co., Ltd., to be at the head of the list of the world's Shipbuilders, with A TOTAL GROSS TONNAGE OF 86,712 TONS, including erections.

The total displacement of vessels built by the firm amounts to close upon Two Million Tons.

List of Shipowners for whom Workman, Clark & Co., Ltd., have built vessels.

THE BRITISH ADMIRALTY.

Allan Line Steamship Co., Ltd.
R. & C. Allan.
Antrim Iron Ore Co., Ltd
Apcar & Co.
Ardan Steamship Co., Ltd.
John Atkinson & Co.
Bantry Bay Steamship Co., Ltd.
Wm. Barbour & Sons.
Ed. Bates & Sons.
Belfast Harbour Commissioners.
Belfast Shipowners' Co., Ltd.
Boyd Bros. & Co.
British and Irish Steam Packet Co.
China Mutual Steam Navigation Co., Ltd.
Clark & Service.
Commissioners of Irish Lights.
Clyde Shipping Co., Ltd.
Coates & Carver.
County Steamship Co., Ltd.
Colvils, Lowden & Co.
J. P. Corry & Co. (Star Line).
Hugh Craig & Co.
Crown Steamship Co., Ltd.
Cunard Steamship Co., Ltd.
James R. Cuthbertson & Co.
Thomas Dixon & Sons.
Dublin Port and Docks Board.

Ellerman Lines, Ltd.
Galbraith & Moorhead.
T. & J. Harrison (Harrison Line).
M. J. Hedley Steamship Co., Ltd.
John Herron & Co.
Wm. Hinde.
Houlder Bros. & Co., Ltd.
R. P. Houston & Co. (Houston Line).
H. Hutton & Co.
P. Iredale & Son.
Irish Shipowners' Co., Ltd. (Lord Line).
Wm. Johnston & Co., Ltd.
Lamport & Holt.
F. Leyland & Co., Ltd.
R. W. Leyland & Co., Ltd.
James Little & Co.
Lough Neagh Ship Co.
David Macbrayne.
J. J. Macfarlane & Co.
R. Mackie & Co.
Marshall, Dodson & Co.
R. Martin & Co.
J. M'Cormick & Co.
John Milligen & Co., Ltd.
Montgomerie & Workman.
Moore Brothers.
Newry Steam Packet Co.

New York and Cuba Steamship Co.
Nippon Yusen Kaisha.
Norddeutscher Lloyd.
Northern Shipowners' Co., Ltd.
Ocean Steamship Co., Ltd.
Peninsular and Oriental Steam Navigation Co.
Wm. Porter & Sons.
Potter Brothers.
Rangoon Port Commissioners.
W. R. Rea.
Wm. Ross & Co.
Royal Mail Steam Packet Co.
H. J. Scott & Co.
Shaw, Savill & Albion Co., Ltd.
George Smith.
George Smith & Sons (City Line).
Smith & Service.
South African Shipping Co.
R. Tedcastle & Co.
Tyser Line, Ltd.
Ulster Steamship Co., Ltd.
United Fruit Company, Boston.
West Australian Steamship Company.
West India & Pacific Steamship Co., Ltd.
Wincott, Cooper & Co.
W. J. Woodside & Co.
J. & A. Wyllie.

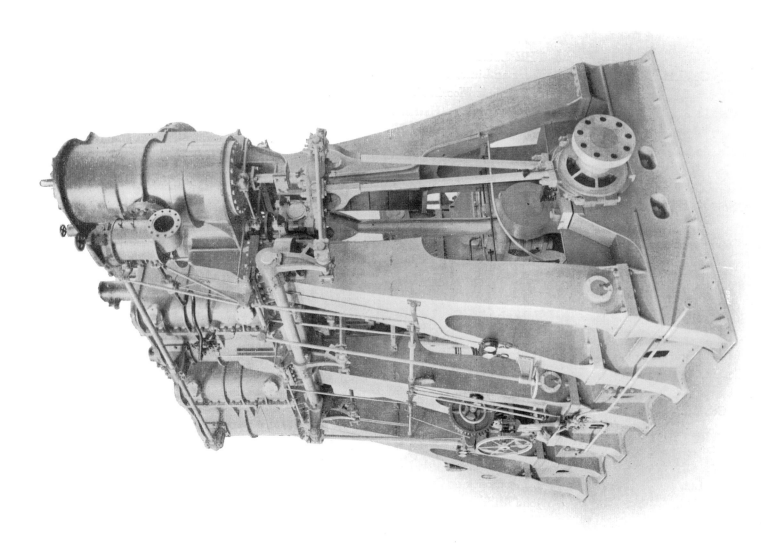

TRIPLE EXPANSION, INVERTED CYLINDER, SURFACE CONDENSING ENGINE,
FOR A TRANSATLANTIC MAIL STEAMER OF 16,000 TONS DISPLACEMENT.

36

ANOTHER VIEW OF THE SAME ENGINES.

"VICTORIAN,"
FIRST TRANSATLANTIC TURBINE STEAMER.

TURBINE STEAMER "VICTORIAN."

GENERAL.

The Turbine steamer "VICTORIAN," now building by Workman, Clark & Co., Ltd., promises to form one of the most noteworthy additions to the mercantile marine for the coming year, and in the following pages will be found a description of the more important features of the vessel.

The "VICTORIAN" will be the finest steamer of the Allan Line, and is intended to be employed in the Canadian Mail Service. The principal dimensions are—length, 540 feet ; breadth, 60 feet ; depth, 42 feet 6 inches. She will be fitted and equipped as a first-class Atlantic passenger steamer, with accommodation for upwards of 1,300 passengers. The vessel is divided by bulkheads into eleven compartments, and these, together with the subdivisions of the double bottom, allow her to have twenty distinct water-tight spaces.

The new vessel is being constructed to the highest class of the British Corporation Registry of Shipping, and the strength of the hull has been specially augmented over the requirements of the Classification Society to meet the heavy weather of the North Atlantic. She will be surveyed and passed by the Board of Trade for a Passenger Certificate, and will also be fitted in conformity with the American laws for passenger steamers.

PASSENGERS.

FIRST CLASS ACCOMMODATION will be provided in houses centrally situated on the bridge and promenade decks, and the distance between decks has been made higher than ordinary to allow of large and lofty state rooms, arranged to accommodate two and three persons, together with a number of self-contained suites of rooms.

THE DINING SALOONS for the first class are placed—one at the fore end of the bridge, fitted with seating accommodation for 200 persons ; the other at the after end of the bridge, with similar seating accommodation ; while on the main deck is fitted the second class saloon.

THE FIRST CLASS MUSIC ROOM, LIBRARY, AND WRITING ROOMS are situated at the fore end of the upper bridge, immediately above the forward dining saloon.

THE FIRST CLASS SMOKE ROOM is a large oak-panelled room, situated at the after end of the promenade deck, with the floor, as in the dining saloons, laid with parquetry.

SECOND CLASS PASSENGERS are accommodated in four berth rooms on the upper and main decks amidships.

THE SECOND CLASS MUSIC ROOM is placed at the after end of the bridge deck ; is handsomely furnished and upholstered, and the walls are panelled in polished hardwood.

THE SECOND CLASS SMOKING ROOM is provided for in a special deck-house built on the upper deck, and having the walls and ceiling tastefully panelled and decorated.

THE THIRD CLASS ACCOMMODATION is arranged in the upper and lower 'tween decks, in four, five, and six-berth cabins, all fitted with patent spring-bottomed beds.

DINING SALOONS, SITTING ROOM, MUSIC ROOM, AND SMOKE ROOMS have also been fitted for the sole use of the third class passengers.

THE MARCONI TELEGRAPHIC appliances have been fitted on board, and there is also provided a complete printing outfit and printing press.

ALL THE ACCOMMODATION is provided with heating arrangements on the most approved principle ; and in all the public rooms and passages numerous radiators are being fitted of an elegant design.

The ship will be fitted with a first-class installation of electric light, the generating power for which is provided by means of three electric engines and dynamos, and mechanical ventilation of the most modern description is being fitted throughout the steamer.

CARGO.

Although the "VICTORIAN" has such a large complement of passengers there is still space available for almost 8,000 tons of cargo, and the facilities for its rapid handling and discharge are of the most efficient description.

On both masts are arranged four large derricks, each capable of lifting up to 7 tons, and these, along with two crane post derricks,

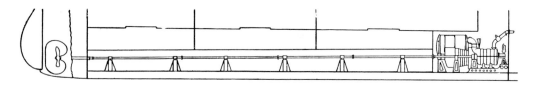

SECTIONAL ELEVATION.

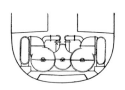

SECTION THROUGH ENGINE
ROOM.

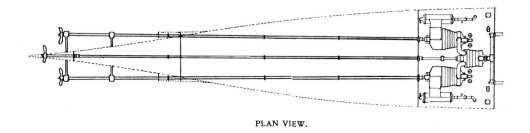

PLAN VIEW.

SECTION AT AFT END.

THE ARRANGEMENT OF THE TURBINE MACHINERY.

make ten in all, for the working of which ten double-cylinder steam winches are supplied.

SPECIAL ATTENTION has been given to the arrangement of the cargo holds; and the ordinary round pillar supports for the decks have been largely discarded in favour of special girders and struts, which leave the holds freer for the reception, storage, and discharge of cargo.

INSULATED CHAMBERS for the carriage of fruit and dairy produce from Canada are provided, in conjunction with Refrigerating plant on the cold air circulation system. The vessel also has sufficient bunker accommodation for the double journey, with an extra allowance of several days in the event of any unforeseen delay, thus obviating all fear of a shortage of fuel.

MACHINERY OF THE "VICTORIAN."

Admirable as are the various arrangements of the steamer for the comfort of the passengers, it is to the machinery of this vessel that special attention will be directed, as the "VICTORIAN" is the first Atlantic liner in connection with which it is proposed to demonstrate the efficiency of the turbine for large steamers.

THE TURBINE OF MESSRS. PARSONS & CO.'s patent has been adopted as the one there is the greatest amount of experience with in both naval and mercantile ships. Messrs. Workman, Clark & Co., Ltd., have acquired the right to build and equip vessels with the Parson turbine, and are laying down the necessary plant, so that the utilization of this engine for passenger and cargo steamers is certain to be rapidly developed in their hands.

THE TURBINE can legitimately claim that, as compared with the reciprocating engine, there is a saving of weight, cost, space, attendance, and upkeep; a complete absence of vibration; a reduced diameter of propellers, giving greater immersion; and an increase of speed, owing to a smaller steam consumption; while the smooth, continuous action of the turbine, with no rubbing surfaces and no thrust friction (for the thrust is taken by the steam itself), makes it an ideal marine engine.

A special design has been adopted of three shafts with one propeller on each, the high-pressure engine driving the centre propeller, while the low-pressures are attached to the outside shafts.

THE PARALLEL FLOW is the type of turbines used, the general course of the steam through them being parallel to the axis of rotation. In streaming through the casing, the steam passes alternate rings of fixed guide blades and moving turbine blades, and having traversed the series in the high-pressure engine, it goes to the low-pressures on either side, and from them finds its way to the condenser as in the ordinary type of engine.

TWO REVERSING TURBINES have been placed in the low-pressure casings, enabling the vessel to go astern when required; and here it should be noted that, in its power of stopping the ship quickly, the turbine claims a great superiority over the reciprocating engine. The peculiar construction of the blades exercises, when the turbines are rotating in a contrary action to the steam which is passing through them, a turning moment two or three times as great as the turning moment when the engines are running in the direction they were made for; whereas in a piston engine there is practically the same force whether the engine is going with the steam or against it. As an instance, the turbine steamer "Queen," when going at 19 knots, was stopped in two and a half times her own length.

THE SPEED of the "VICTORIAN" will be a great advance on any other steamer on the same route, and it is confidently expected that, under favourable conditions, the voyage to Canada will be shortened by over a day; so that this vessel will prove an important item in the development of our growing Colonial trade.

TO CONCLUDE: the application of the turbine system has proceeded beyond the experimental stage; it is a confirmed success; and now its application to the largest Atlantic liners marks an epoch in the progress of one of the most noteworthy inventions which have helped to confirm this country in its undisputed claim to maritime supremacy

T.S.S. "IONIAN," FIRST-CLASS CANADIAN MAIL STEAMER, FOR MESSRS. THE ALLAN LINE STEAMSHIP CO., L™

H.M. FIRST-CLASS CRUISER "ST. GEORGE," UNDERGOING COMPLETE OVERHAUL.

T.S.S. "DRAYTON GRANGE" AND "OSWESTRY GRANGE."
10,000 TONS MEAT-CARRYING STEAMERS FOR MESSRS. HOULDER BROS., LTD.

STERNPOST.

"PELEUS," "TYDEUS," "TELEMACHUS," AND "JASON": FOUR SISTER SHIPS BUILT FOR MESSRS. THE OCEAN STEAMSHIP CO., LTD.
DEAD-WEIGHT CAPACITY, 10,000 TONS.
TOTAL NUMBER OF VESSELS BUILT FOR THIS COMPANY, 21.

S.S. "CITY OF ATHENS," PASSENGER AND CARGO LINER TO INDIA FOR MESSRS. GEO. SMITH & SONS, LTD.
GROSS TONNAGE, 6,000 TONS.

T.S.S. "RATHLIN HEAD."
10,000 TONS DEAD-WEIGHT CARRIER FOR ATLANTIC TRADE.

T.S.S. "WAYFARER," 13,000 TONS DEAD-WEIGHT CARRIER FOR MESSRS. T. & J. HARRISON.
TOTAL NUMBER OF VESSELS BUILT FOR THIS COMPANY, 10.

CAISSON FOR GRAVING DOCK.

A LAUNCH.

ONE OF THE MODELS.

FOUR-MASTED BARQUE.

S.S. "CITY OF CALCUTTA," INDIAN PASSENGER AND CARGO LINER FOR MESSRS. THE ELLERMAN LINES, LTD.
GROSS TONNAGE, 7,500 TONS.
TOTAL NUMBER OF VESSELS BUILT FOR THIS COMPANY, 15.

S.S. "COLONIAL"

S.S. "COUNSELLOR."

8,000 TONS DEAD-WEIGHT CARRIERS FOR MESSRS. T. & J. HARRISON.

51

T.S.S. "PERA" AND "PALMA," 11,000 TONS DEAD-WEIGHT CARRIERS FOR MESSRS. THE PENINSULAR AND ORIENTAL STEAM NAVIGATION CO., LTD.

"PALMA" ON THE STOCKS.

ON THE T.S.S. "PALMA."

T.S.S. "NIWARU" AND "MARERE."
10,000 TONS MEAT-CARRYING STEAMERS FOR MESSRS. THE TYSER LINE, LTD.

T.S.S. "KEEMUN."
12,000 TONS DEAD WEIGHT CARRIER FOR THE CHINA MUTUAL S. N. CO., LTD.

S.S. "GREGORY APCAR."
INDIAN COASTING PASSENGER AND CARGO STEAMER FOR MESSRS. APCAR & CO., CALCUTTA.
GROSS TONNAGE, 5,000 TONS.

MESSRS. J. P. CORRY & CO.'S S.S. "STAR OF IRELAND,"
BUILT FOR THE NEW ZEALAND AND SOUTH AMERICAN FROZEN MEAT TRADE.

58

LAUNCH OF THE "STAR OF IRELAND."

59

S.S. "TITIAN" AND "TINTORETTO," SOUTH AMERICAN TRADERS, BUILT FOR MESSRS. LAMPORT & HOLT.
GROSS TONNAGE, 4,300 TONS.

S.S. "LOCKSLEY HALL," BUILT FOR MESSRS. THE HALL LINE, LTD.
DEAD-WEIGHT CARRYING CAPACITY, 8,000 TONS.

END OF 1903 VOLUME

[i]

THE BRITISH (GUEST KEEN BALDWINS) IRON & STEEL Co. Ltd.

Registered & Head Office: **PORT TALBOT**

London Office :

**66 CANNON ST.
LONDON
E.C. 4**

Works :

**PORT TALBOT
MARGAM
CARDIFF
DOWLAIS**

VIEW OF BANK—"HEAVY PLATE MILL"—PORT TALBOT.

In the Building of Ships—

Specify **THE BRITISH (GUEST KEEN BALDWINS) IRON & STEEL CO. LTD.** for

SECTIONS :: PLATES :: AND BOILER PLATES

INSULATION

FOR EVERY TYPE OF MODERN REFRIGERATED CARGO CARRIER

GREGSON & C° L^{TD}

FELSTED ROAD, LONDON, E.16.

TELEGRAMS:

"GREGIDES, VICDOCK, LONDON."

TELEPHONE:

ALBERT DOCK 2170 (2 LINES)

[v]

(ESTABLISHED 1864.   INCORPORATED 1908)

THOMAS DIXON & SONS
LIMITED

Timber and Slate Importers and Merchants

An important old-established representative firm of wholly British Origin and Ownership.   Founded nearly 70 years ago by the late Thomas Dixon.   Is to-day one of the oldest and most prominent local Houses in this Trade.   Has extensive premises completely equipped with modern machinery and the latest appliances for highly efficient service including Saw Mills; Planing and Moulding Mills; Creosoting to the most up-to-date specification.   The firm has a large business connection in Home, Colonial and Foreign Markets.

Registered General Offices—

MILEWATER ROAD, BELFAST, NORTHERN IRELAND

Telegraphic Address—DIXONS, BELFAST.   *Telephone No. 2727 (5 lines) BELFAST.*

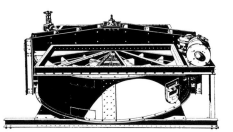

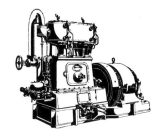

HOWDEN FANS
FOR FORCED AND
INDUCED DRAUGHT

HOWDEN
LJUNGSTROM AIR PRE-
HEATERS

HOWDEN
VORTEX
DUST COLLECTORS

HOWDEN
HIGH-SPEED STEAM
ENGINES

Half a Century ago

James Howden designed the first installation of hot air forced draught. Since then the most important steamships in the world, including those built by

Workman Clark (1928) Ltd.,

have had

HOWDEN Auxiliaries.

FANS
Forced and Induced Draught.

FURNACE FRONTS
for Coal, Oil and Pulverised Fuel.

AIR PREHEATERS
Tubular, Turbulent Flow and Ljungstrom.

DUST COLLECTORS
for clean decks.

JAMES HOWDEN & CO., LTD. (Since 1854), GLASGOW

HOWDEN

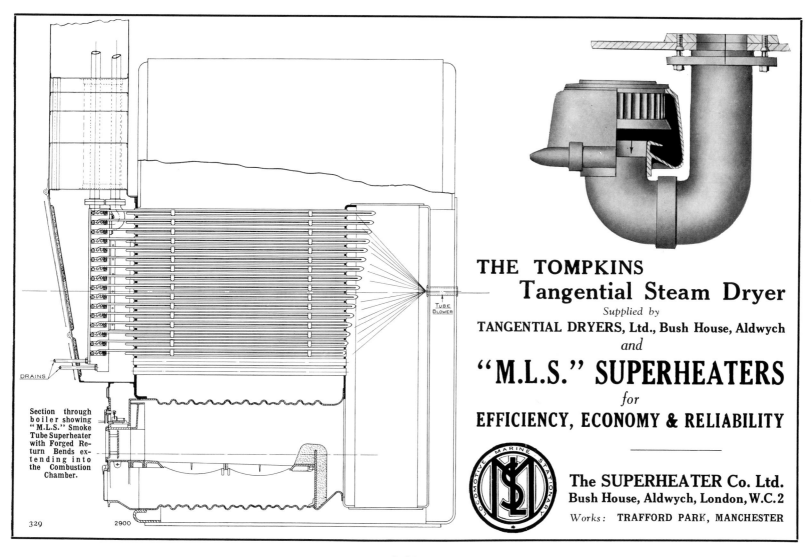

DRAINS

Section through boiler showing "M.L.S." Smoke Tube Superheater with Forged Return Bends extending into the Combustion Chamber.

329   2900

TUBE BLOWER

THE TOMPKINS
Tangential Steam Dryer

Supplied by

TANGENTIAL DRYERS, Ltd., Bush House, Aldwych

and

"M.L.S." SUPERHEATERS

for

EFFICIENCY, ECONOMY & RELIABILITY

[xi]

'SIROCCO' PRODUCTS

Write for "Sirocco Products" which summarises in pictures our manufacturing activities.

Centrifugal & Propeller Fans. Aeroto (trade mark) Patent Screw Fans. Air Heaters, Washers and Automatic Air Conditioning Units. "Davidson" dust & flue dust Collectors. Pneumatic Conveying Plant etc. etc.

OUR ACCUMULATED EXPERIENCE IS AT YOUR SERVICE.

DAVIDSON & CO. LTD.
SIROCCO ENGINEERING WORKS, BELFAST

"Established in 1881"

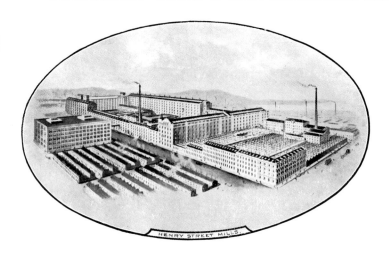
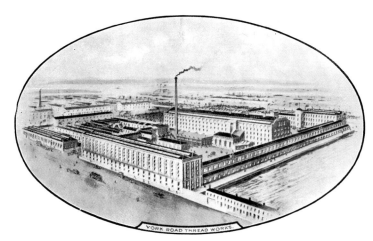

A Ship's popularity with the Travelling Public depends a great deal on its equipment, and in this connection the LINEN FURNISHINGS form one of the most important items. Nothing is more attractive and comforting (for the Tables and Bedrooms) than a well-selected stock of the finest Fabrics, produced by a firm of world-wide repute. Such a firm is

York Street Flax Spinning Co., Ltd., of Belfast, N. Ireland

Established over 100 years, and owning the largest Linen producing plant in the world, the name "YORK STREET" is famous wherever ships sail. They have been for generations suppliers of Linens to all the large Steamship Lines, and can undertake anything made in Linen—Pantry and Kitchen Cloths, Towels, Sheets and Pillow Cases, Tea Cloths, Damasks, Cloths, Napkins, etc.

Enquiries are invited for samples and quotations.

SHIPBUILDING AT BELFAST

Printed and Published for

WORKMAN CLARK (1928) LTD.

Shipbuilders, BELFAST

by

ED. J. BURROW & CO. LTD.

LONDON AND CHELTENHAM

First Printed In 1933

Introduction

Something of that sense of romance which clings to stories of the sea is felt also as one reads the story of a great shipbuilding enterprise—for without shipbuilding no-one would have had stories of the sea to tell or to read !

Here, however, romance is but an undercurrent, and the main swell is concerned with such eminently practical things as hulls and decks, engines, winches, masts, and all the other numerous products of shipbuilding and engineering skill which go to make and maintain the world-wide trade of a great seafaring people.

A very long story indeed might be written about the Workman Clark organisation, for its history would furnish material not for one volume but for a series. We prefer, however, to consider the time and patience of those friends—present and prospective—into whose hands this book will fall, and to present them rather with a series of briefly-told episodes, leaving the many pictures of good ships of all types to amplify the story.

WORKMAN CLARK (1928) LTD.

Q.M.V. "BERMUDA"

20,000 ton Passenger Liner for the New York-Bermuda Service of Messrs. Furness Withy & Co. Ltd.

Back in the 'Eighties

Fifty-four years ago—in the spring of 1880—an event charged with significance few could then foresee, took place in Belfast. It was the laying of the keel of the first ship constructed by Workman Clark—the first of a vast progeny that now runs into many hundreds and is distributed over all the seas of the world.

The intervening period of more than half a century has seen the steady progress of a firm which now ranks among the world's premier shipbuilding and engineering industries. The steady and constantly increasing outflow of ships from this famous Belfast yard has been made possible by an equally constant inflow of energy, foresight and imagination on the part of those responsible for its inception and growth. These qualities have steered the business through changing periods of prosperity and depression up to and beyond its re-birth in 1928 as Workman Clark (1928) Limited.

T.S.S. "OTRANTO" AND "ORVIETO"
Two pre-war 15,000-ton Passenger Liners for the Australian Mail Service of the Orient Steam Navigation Co.

Modest Beginnings

The original shipyard occupied four acres on the north side of the River Lagan. The original staff comprised only 150 men, whose output for the first year consisted of two steamers of 800 tons. But the vision of greater things dawned early in the history of the business, and within two years the founders—Mr. Frank Workman and Mr. George Clark—had the satisfaction of seeing vessels 400 feet in length rising on their stocks.

Increasing business compelled continuous extensions until in 1891 the four-acre yard had grown to fourteen acres. In those days sailing ships and paddle steamers still formed an important part of the firm's production alongside construction of screw steamers in numbers which showed a steady tendency to predominate over the older forms of craft. Up to this point, the business was entirely a shipbuilding one, the engines and boilers for the steamers being supplied by Clydeside engineers.

Nos. 533 and 534
Two Twin-Screw 12,000-ton Refrigerated Motor Cargo Liners for Messrs. The New Zealand Shipping Co. Ltd.

Some Important Landmarks

It was in 1891 that the important decision was taken to add an engineering works to the shipbuilding yard. Mr. Charles Allen, of Glasgow, joined the Board as Engineering Director and founded the Engineering Department which has ever since progressed steadily side by side with the Shipbuilding Department.

Another important point was reached two years later, when the business of Messrs. McIlwaine & MacColl was acquired. This firm had been engaged in shipbuilding and engineering since 1863, and the presence of their Abercorn Engine Works close to the Workman Clark Engineering Works facilitated the process of absorption. This move brought the extent of the Workman Clark yards and works up to 40 acres.

By 1895, the annual output had advanced from the original 800 tons to no less than 34,000 tons, carrying the firm to fourth place among the leading shipbuilding industries. The original staff of 150 had swelled to 3,500 men.

T.S.S. "VANDYCK" AND "VOLTAIRE"
Two 530-ft. Passenger Liners, built for the Liverpool-Brazil Express Service of Messrs. Lamport & Holt.

Into the New Century

In 1902 the establishment covered 50 acres, and headed the tonnage returns of the world's shipbuilders with an output of 75,800 tons. This proud distinction came again in 1909 with 88,200 tons gross.

By 1920 the acreage had increased to 100 and the pay-roll to 10,000. Three additional building berths had been constructed in the North Yard, the largest of which could accommodate a vessel of over 1,000 feet in length.

This year, 1920, saw the business pass from its founders into other hands ; but old associations were maintained while new connections were established. The subsequent industrial depression struck the business a heavy, but not a fatal, blow. Like its own good ships, it weathered the storm although it had to turn into port for re-fitting. This took the form of a re-organisation of the Company's affairs, and in March, 1928, it set forth again as Workman Clark (1928) Limited.

THE NORTH SHIPYARD

Pre-War

1930

Re-incarnation

The prime mover in the formation of Workman Clark (1928) Limited was Mr. William Strachan, a Director and Secretary of the old Company. A number of old friends of the business had rallied to his support and in assuming the Chairmanship of the new enterprise, he had the advantage of the able and loyal co-operation of Mr. William Lovett and Mr. James Wilkie, both of whom had been associated with the old Company for many years.

It was particularly encouraging to those who now took the helm of this thoroughly modern and well-equipped vessel, that two of the oldest friends of the business—Messrs. Alfred Holt, Ltd., and the Ellerman Lines—should be among the first to place orders with the new Company. These orders gave a successful launching to the new enterprise and brought the business indicator round once more to the cheerful point of "Full Ahead."

T.S.S. "ULYSSES"

600-ft. Passenger and Cargo Liner, which, with her sister ship, T.S.S. "Nestor," were pioneers of the present day popular one-class cabin vessels. Built for the Australian Service of Messrs. Alfred Holt & Co.

S.S. "CITY OF NAGPUR"

A Passenger and Cargo Liner and Flag Ship of the Ellerman Lines.

The Barometer Rises

Many and varied were the orders for ships and machinery that followed the establishment of the new regime. The number of ships constructed up to date jumped from 502 in 1928 to 536 at the end of 1933, representing a total value of over $5\frac{1}{4}$ million pounds and a gross tonnage of 190,000—a remarkable five-years' record, particularly in view of the continued depression in industry and consequent keenness of competition.

Such progress had naturally compelled further extensions. The firm's capacity for economic production has been almost doubled by introducing more efficient machinery, while output has been speeded up and made more economic by the adoption of a new standard of fabrication sequence, without any sacrifice of strength or quality in workmanship.

The survey of the firm's products given on subsequent pages, read in conjunction with the outline just given of its growth, confirm its unchanged policy of turning out nothing but the best in workmanship and material.

S.S. "CEFALU"

S.S. "GATUN"

(Above)
Two Passenger and
Fruit Vessels for the
West Indian Service
of the Standard Fruit
and Steamship Co.

(Left)
For the same Owners
a 17-knot Transatlantic
Fruiter with Exhaust
Turbo - Electric Drive
operating in conjunc-
tion with a four-cylin-
der Triple Expansion
Engine.

S.S. "ERIN"

Sail and Steam

History often repeats itself, but in the case of Workman Clark it reversed itself. That is to say, the firm had built 21 steamers before constructing their first sailing ship, the "Fort George," a four-masted barque of 2,600 tons deadweight, constructed in 1884 for Clark & Service.

During the next twelve years, however, no less than 32 sailing vessels were built, many of these being of the four-masted barque type and all "handy sized vessels," as they were termed, varying from 1,000 tons to 3,600 tons deadweight. Unfortunately, few pictorial records of these stately craft have been preserved. They rendered as good service in their own quiet ways as the magnificent steamers now being built by the firm render in theirs. One of them, built for Galbraith & Moorhead, and originally named the "Lauriston," is still doing useful work for Soviet owners under the new name of "Tovarisch."

"DUNDONALD," "BESSFIELD" AND "CROWN OF GERMANY"

Three of the 36 Sailing Vessels built in the latter part of the Nineteenth Century.

Repeat Orders are Good Evidence!

Now for a matter in which history *has* repeated itself. There could be no better testimony to consistently fine quality than the firm's long succession of repeat orders by satisfied clients.

No less than 51 vessels have been built for the Blue Funnel Line and Associated Companies of Messrs. Alfred Holt & Co., while among other large fleets have been : United Fruit Co. (40 vessels), Cunard-Commonwealth & Dominion Line, Ltd., including J. P. Corry & Co. Ltd. and the Tyser Line (33 vessels), Ellerman Lines, Ltd. (26) and Lloyd Brasiliero (21). Thus 171 vessels out of 536 have been produced for five customers. A further 110 are accounted for by the repeated orders of 16 other firms, including such famous names as Andrew Weir & Co., the P. & O. Co., the R.M.S.P. Co., the British India Steam Navigation Co., Lamport and Holt, Shaw Savill & Albion Co. Ltd., Elders & Fyffes, Booth Line, Furness, Withy & Co., Blue Star Line, Orient Steam Navigation Co., Union Castle Line, Harrison Line, etc.

An impressive list !—yet by no means an exhaustive one.

MODEL OF T.M.V. "ISIPINGO"
"Isipingo," "Inchanga," and "Incomati"
Three 15-knot vessels for the India-Cape Passenger and Cargo Service of Messrs. Andrew Weir & Co.

Specialisation in Ships

The evolution of the Mercantile Marine has been governed by many considerations apart from questions of dimensions, machinery and speed.

Broadly speaking, shipping to-day falls under two main heads :— (1) Vessels employed on definite routes ; and (2) those employed for general cargo work on indefinite routes. The former and higher class includes not only passenger-and-mail boats and passenger-and-cargo boats, but also regular service liners carrying meat, cotton, fruit, oil, coal and other specialised cargoes. The second class includes general cargo carriers and "tramps."

The days when shipbuilders built ships to instructions which were only concerned with size, equipment and cost belong to the past. Nowadays, almost every ship is built for a definite use, and this is a vital factor in governing design. Any loss in general adaptability resulting from this specialisation is more than counterbalanced by the increased economic soundness of carrying, say, meat or oil in ships specially built for meat or oil as the case may be.

T.S.S. "KOSMOS II"

Two views of a 23,000-ton Bulk Oil Carrier and Whaling Factory, which, with her sister ship, S.S. "Kosmos," is the largest vessel of this class in the world.

(Above) On trial in Belfast Lough, June, 1931.

(Left) Stern view showing slipway and aperture.

Passenger Vessels

The same detailed study of special requirements which had been devoted to vessels destined to carry certain types of cargo was also given to the development of passenger boats. Many vessels of this latter class built in the Belfast yards have been the means of successfully inaugurating new services for some of the largest ship-owning firms and of establishing those firms in favour among the travelling public.

It was the T.S.S. "Aeneas" which introduced the name of Alfred Holt & Co. to passengers travelling between the United Kingdom and Australia ; the T.S.S. "Vandyck" inaugurated an express service between Liverpool and Brazil for Lamport & Holt ; the Q.M.V. "Bermuda" successfully established the luxury trade between New York and the Bermudas. And now the three T.M.V.'s "Isipingo," "Inchanga," and "Incomati" are destined this spring (1934) to inaugurate a fast high-class passenger and cargo service between India and the Cape for Andrew Weir & Co.

These are but a few of many pioneering achievements that could be instanced from the firm's records.

"ARAGUAYA"

A large Mail and Passenger Liner for the South American Service of the Royal Mail Steam Packet Co. Ltd.

T.S.S. "VICTORIAN"

The first large Turbine Passenger Liner built in 1903 for the Atlantic Passenger Service of Messrs. J. & A. Allan & Co.

NORTH SHIPYARD

ALEXANDRA

NEW DOCK FITTING OUT BASIN

WORKS
AND DRY DOCKS

SOUTH SHIPYARD

ATER FITTING OUT BASIN

Revolutionising Fruit Transport

In 1902 Workman Clark reviewed the carriage of fruit cargoes. Previously, fruit could only be carried on short runs and the vessels relied on natural ventilation by ventilator cowls which, with wood-sheathed weather decks and a wood lining on the ship's sides, helped to ensure even temperature.

This system, with improvements, is still in use on short-trip fruiters, but further means of ventilation was clearly necessary for the successful transport of fruit on long voyages, particularly between countries of varying temperatures. Workman Clark, therefore, developed the insulated and refrigerated fruit carrier; they were, apparently, the first to apply refrigeration to fruit transport.

Thus began in 1903 their long association with the United Fruit Company of Boston, whose vessels comprise "The Great White Fleet." One of these vessels, the "San Jose," built in 1904, was the first wholly refrigerated fruit carrier. Of the many fine vessels built for this Company, probably the most interesting is the "Musa," built in 1930, a 17-knot turbo-electric drive vessel, which, with the "Erin," also of 17 knots and built in 1932 for the Standard Fruit and Steamship Company of New Orleans, are among the largest and fastest fruit carriers afloat.

"SAN BENITO"

"SIXAOLA"

"TOLOA"

"MUSA"

Four examples of Passenger and Fruit Vessels built for the "Great White Fleet" of the United Fruit Co. The "San Benito" has the distinction of being the first vessel built in the United Kingdom to have Turbo-Electric Propelling Machinery, and the "Musa," with a speed of 17 knots, is one of the fastest Fruit Carriers afloat. It is interesting to note that since the formation of the Company in 1880, 60 vessels for the carriage of fruit have been built, and of these 40 were to the order of the United Fruit Co.

Cargo Liners

In the construction of the cargo liner type of vessel, Workman Clark enjoy an enviable reputation. In a table published by "The Shipping World" some time ago this firm headed the list of cargo liner builders with a total tonnage of 543,733 representing 68 vessels.

Tanker ships built by the firm serve such well-known oil transport companies as British Tankers Ltd., Anglo-American Oil Co. Ltd., Anglo-Saxon Petroleum Co. Ltd., and Andrew Weir & Co. They built the two largest bulk oil carriers in the world—"Kosmos I" (21,000 tons) and "Kosmos II" (23,000 tons)—for the Kosmos Whaling Co. Another special order was the "Appleleaf," a fast fleet oiler for the Admiralty.

Many high-class bulk cargo carriers have been constructed for such well-known owners as Andrew Weir & Co., T. & J. Harrison, G. Heyn & Sons, Ltd., Clark & Service, Court Line, Sir William Reardon Smith, and the Berwindmoor Steamship Co. Ltd., for whom the "Berwindmoor," a 10,000 tons deadweight topside tanker collier, was built in 1923.

T.M.V. "AGAMEMNON"

Leaving the Shipyard for trials. A large Cargo Liner
built in 1929 for Messrs. Alfred Holt & Co.

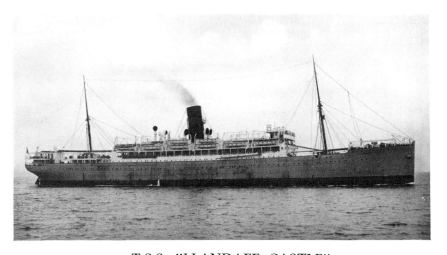

T.S.S. "LLANDAFF CASTLE"

Passenger and Cargo Liner for the Union Castle
Steam Navigation Co.

T.M.V. "PORT FREEMANTLE"

10,000-ton Refrigerated Cargo Liner and one of many similar
vessels built during the past 40 years for the Commonwealth & Dominion Line and Associated Companies.

T.S.S. "CARNARVONSHIRE"

A large Refrigerated Cargo Liner for the
Royal Mail Steam Packet Co. Ltd.

Individuality

First-class shipbuilding knows no mass-production comparable to the building of land vessels—that is to say, motor cars—by which the products of one firm are easily recognised by their stock-pattern design.

So diverse have been the requirements of owners, both for passenger and cargo vessels, that almost every vessel turned out has been the only vessel of its precise kind. There has, of course, been a proportion of "sister ships" among the many hundreds built by the firm, but these represent a minority. The outstanding characteristic has been individuality of design. This is clearly shown by our illustrations.

There is little in the external appearance of these vessels to indicate that they are entirely the product of one firm. In fact, the only "family likeness" between them is one not obvious to the layman but well recognised by the expert—the fine quality of material and workmanship common to them all.

T.S.S. "ORANIA"

Turbine Passenger Liner for the South American Service of the Koninklijke Hollandsche Lloyd.

T.S.S. "ESSEQUIBO" & "EBRO"

Two Passenger and Cargo Liners for the Pacific Steam Navigation Co. Ltd.

A Case in Point

One of the best examples of that individuality referred to overleaf was afforded by the two fine steamers "Otranto" and "Orvieto," built over twenty years ago for the Orient Line.

This famous line required fine ships for passenger and mail service on the Australian trade. Two were ordered from Workman Clark, while three Clyde shipbuilders received orders for one each. All four builders were given a free hand in design so long as the basic specification of the owners was complied with. The three Clydeside builders all adhered to a similar type, but the Belfast firm enterprisingly adopted a design of its own. This met with signal success, not only in popularity with travellers but also in superior speed and gracefulness of appearance. The "Otranto" and "Orvieto" came to be regarded as the "star ships" of the Orient fleet. The "Orvieto" remained in commission on the Orient Line's service for twenty years, only being sold out of the fleet as recently as 1931, while her sister, the "Otranto," was sunk during the war by mines off the North Coast of Ireland while acting as an auxiliary cruiser and transport. It is interesting to note that this vessel took part in the disastrous naval engagement of Coronel.

WORLD'S RIVETING RECORD

WORKMAN CLARK—JUNE 1918

	NUMBER OF RIVETS	ACCUMULATING TOTALS
1ST HOUR	1167	1167
2ND ..	1101	2268
3RD ..	1071	3339
4TH ..	1187	4526
5TH ..	1267	5793
6TH ..	1328	7121
7TH ..	1409	8530
8TH ..	1276	9806
9TH ..	1403	11209
TOTAL		

This is a photograph of the board on which was recorded the hour by hour totals of rivets driven home by J. Moir, and include only the actual numbers as passed by Lloyds and British Corporation Surveyors.

Workman Clark are very proud of the skill and organisation which resulted in the tremendous total of 11,209 rivets by one man in a working day, a Shipbuilding record which will probably stand for all time.

Setting a New Standard

The sailing ship was classified into many distinct types as regards size and design, but in most cases it was *not* a specialised vessel so far as use was concerned.

With the passing of the sailing ship, Workman Clark considered what types of vessels they would build during the oncoming period that was clearly going to be a period of specialisation. This careful survey of future prospects led to the selection of certain types of vessel, and the adaptation of the firm's plant to deal with those special types.

The definite study thus directed towards improvement and progress soon earned its reward. The construction of the "Niwaru" and the "Wayfarer" in 1902 constituted a landmark in the history not only of this firm but of British shipbuilding generally, for it can be said that these vessels set a new standard for colonial meat and cotton carriers respectively.

"ARANKOLA"

"EGRA"

Passenger and Cargo Vessels for the
Eastern Service of the British India
Steam Navigation Co.

Versatility plus Specialisation

The modern policy of constructing ships for special purposes instead of for indiscriminate use has caused shipbuilders to specialise in building ships of certain types. This has to some extent been the policy of Workman Clark (1928) Ltd. The firm's records show a high measure of versatility, but they also show the construction of many ships of highly specialised types. The fact that these latter ships have not been mere single instances but in many cases repeat orders shows that the firm's capacity for specialised building has been amply proved.

It has always been the policy of the firm to study at first hand the various trades which its vessels are destined to serve—not only the nature of the goods to be carried, and the direct problems (such as cold storage) arising therefrom, but also the connected problems of loading, stowage, discharge, limitations in size imposed either by the anticipated cargoes or by local conditions at home and foreign ports.

T.M.V. "IRISBANK"
One of a group of four fast Cargo Liners for
Messrs. Andrew Weir & Co.

T.S.S. "DELTA"
A Passenger Liner for the Peninsular & Oriental
Steam Navigation Co. Ltd.

T.S.S. "MINAS GERAES"
One of a group of six special vessels for the Passenger
and Coastal Service of the Lloyd Brazileiro.

Ship Repairing and Tanker Maintenance

Ship repairing is an important department of Workman Clark (1928) Ltd., and one which has many interesting contracts to its credit.

Perhaps the most interesting task undertaken in this direction was the lengthening and re-engining of the M.V. "La Marea" (now re-named "Darien"). The existing Diesel machinery was removed, the vessel lengthened by 27 feet 6 inches, and a new installation of high-pressure turbo-electric machinery fitted.

A special feature has developed in the Repair Department, namely, the repair and maintenance of oil tank tonnage. During recent years, this side of repair work has been carefully studied in order to give as prompt and efficient service as possible, with the result that many oil tank vessels pass through the hands of this Department in the course of a year. The popularity of the Belfast yard for this purpose has been aided by the fact that the Port dues are almost the lowest in the United Kingdom.

M.V. "CHESAPEAKE"
A 13,500 tons deadweight Oil Tanker. Built for
The Anglo-American Oil Co. Ltd.

Equipment and Organisation

Only very briefly can we deal with the internal organisation of Workman Clark (1928) Ltd. This consists of four separate plants, located on both sides of the River Lagan, the administrative head-quarters and drawing offices being situated on The North Twin Island in conjunction with the North or Main Yard. The whole lay-out of the plant has been very carefully studied with a view to facilitating rapid construction and to eliminate all avoidable movement of either men or materials.

The island site of North Yard has the advantage of providing conveniently situated fitting-out berths ; these are well equipped with both travelling and stationary cranes and can accommodate (simultaneously) six vessels in the fitting-out stage. The main fitting-out berth is probably one of the finest of its kind in existence, lying alongside the various workshops which are connected to it by gangways.

A special feature of the Workman Clark shipyard is the Platers' Shed with its thoroughly modern plant, including a battery of "one-man" punches.

A view of one of the
North Yard Fitting-out
Berths, showing a large
passenger vessel fitting
out alongside, with the
South Yard and Alex-
andra Dock Works in
the background.

Building Slips and Workshops

The building slips of North Yard, eight in number, are heavily piled and No. 8 can take vessels up to over 1,000 feet long. Each slip is served by tower cranes except Nos. 1 and 2, where, it is interesting to note, the masts of the famous "Great Eastern" act as crane and derrick posts. Large travelling gantry cranes are mounted two on each side of No. 8 slip and smaller ones between slips Nos. 5, 6 and 7 ; fixed gantry cranes are installed between Nos. 3 and 4.

In a large shed specially built for oil tank work, whole bulkheads, deck-houses, etc., are drawn out on the wood floor, the plates being punched by templates lifted from the floor and finally "fitted" before going to the slips. Each workshop has its special features— none more interesting, perhaps, than the Joiners' Shop, a wonder of modern methods.

The South Yard, connected with North Yard by ferry, is smaller but laid out on similar lines, with five slips capable of taking vessels up to 600 feet long.

View of North Yard, showing "Kosmos II" on No. 8 Slip. This slip is capable of accommodating vessels of over 1,000 feet in length.

The Engineering Works

Here we come to another subject of large dimensions and manifold sub-divisions which can only be briefly summarised. The engineering establishment, continually extended, improved, and maintained in first-class order during its more than 40 years' existence, comprises both the Main and Auxiliary Engine Works, on the Co. Down side of the river. From both works machinery is easily conveyed to the fitting-out berths, where mammoth cranes with lifting capacities up to 150 tons lift boilers and engines on to the vessels. The administrative, commercial and technical offices adjoin the Main Engine Works, the drawing office being well-designed for natural lighting—a very desirable feature.

The firm's own modernised Cyclops Foundry at Whiteinch, Glasgow, can deal with all the iron castings required for propelling machinery, etc., and has been particularly successful in solving the highly technical problems presented by castings for Diesel engines. There are pattern-making shops here as well as at Belfast.

Heavy forgings are obtained direct from the steel works, but light forgings and all smithwork are manufactured within the firm's own plant.

8-cyl. Workman Clark-Sulzer Diesel Engine installed in the Anglo-American Oil Tanker M.V. "Chesapeake."

Notable Engineering Achievements

Many notable pioneering achievements must be credited to the Engineering Department, especially in connection with the application of the turbine engine, turbo-electric machinery and the present popular exhaust turbo-electric drive, operating in conjunction with ordinary reciprocating machinery.

The Allan Liner, "Victorian" (afterwards the C.P.R. Liner, "Marloch") was the first turbine-driven ocean-going mail steamer. Her successful performance influenced the Cunard Company's decision to build the "Lusitania" and "Mauretania" as turbine ships. Later, on the introduction of double-reduction geared turbines, Workman Clark introduced the Nodal Drive, which to a large degree eliminated torsional vibration in the propeller shafts of vessels so fitted.

The "San Benito," built in 1921, was the first British-built vessel installed with turbo-electric propelling machinery. This proved very successful, although only within recent years has the system really found favour—due probably to the rapid development of the internal combustion engine. The firm is familiar with this latter class, and manufactures the Workman Clark Sulzer Diesel engine.

Turbine Machinery.

Engines, Machinery and Boilers

The Engine Shop, embracing machine-shop, tool-room, erecting and brass-finishing departments, is a capacious and lofty single-floor building, extremely well lighted, all heavy machines being served by overhead travelling cranes, together with many jib cranes. In an annexe is a fully-equipped sand-blasting room. The Erecting Shop contains full testing plant.

The Machine Shop is complete with machine tools of every description. We cannot attempt to enumerate these, but may mention that the largest shafting lathe takes in 55 feet between centres, the crank-shaft lathe 25 feet 6 inches between centres, while the largest turbine-boring machine has an 8-feet diameter capacity and unlimited length.

The Boiler Shop has been designed and fully equipped for making cylindrical and water-tube boilers, smoke-boxes, funnels, condensers, tank-work of all descriptions, general steel constructional work and other branches. Large plate furnaces, flanging machines and hydraulic plate-bending and riveting machines are installed, while oxy-acetylene welding and electric welding processes have been perfected to a remarkable degree.

Two views of the Quadruple Expansion Reciprocating Engine built for S.S. "City of Nagpur."

Auxiliary Engine Works and Repairs

The Auxiliary Engine Works are admirably equipped for the manufacture of high-class auxiliary equipment, such as condensing plants, oil-burning installations, centrifugal circulating pumps, high-speed auxiliary engines for pumps and electric generators, open and enclosed steam winches, water-tight doors, etc.

Among numerous other branches of the extensive plant may be mentioned the Plumbers' Shop, where iron and steel pipe work is carried out on an extensive scale. In addition to the usual equipment of a plumbers' shop, the plant comprises drilling, screwing, sand-rapping, and grinding machines, hydraulic hoists, hydraulic pipe - bending machine, and electric and oxy - acetylene welding equipment.

Finally, we may refer to the fact that for the repair work previously alluded to in our review of the firm's activities the plant is especially well organised to handle repair contracts with that speed which is an essential factor in minimising loss to owners while ships are idle. A special feature here is the liberal installation of pneumatic plant.

WINCHES

A product of the Auxiliary Engineering
Department, Abercorn Engine Works.

On War Service

A full account of Workman Clark's activities during the Great War would make a big book, for during that period 1,396 vessels were handled either for building, repairing or overhauling. These ranged from battle-cruisers to patrol boats, and from stately liners to boom defence and "Q" boats.

Merchant ships in various stages of construction during the War totalled 95,000 tons. Adding the tonnage of the various other vessels dealt with, the aggregate tonnage completed was 260,000. After completing merchant vessels in hand, the firm were occupied solely with Admiralty orders. These raised immensely varied problems, the successful solution of which is a tribute to the resource and workmanship of the staff and employees.

Among the more famous vessels dealt with were the battle-cruiser "Invincible," battleships "Africa," "Albemarle," "Britannia," "Commonwealth," and "Revenge"; cruisers included the "Hampshire," which sailed from Belfast to carry Lord Kitchener on his last voyage. So many torpedo destroyers, submarines, patrol vessels and mine-sweepers were added to the list that the vessels dealt with approximated one for every day of the War.

H.M.S. "WINDFLOWER"

Blisters, Paravanes and "Q" Boats

The first "blisters" and the first paravanes were fitted by Workman Clark; the chain of barrage vessels for the Straits of Dover was built by them. The famous "Q" boats were built here; monitors for the Dardanelles were completely built in eight weeks; hospital ships for Mesopotamia and boats to carry ammunition to the Western Front were among other orders.

A cargo ship, the "Sandhurst," was converted into a T.B.D. depot ship; passenger and cargo liners were transformed into hospital ships or auxiliary cruisers. One 8,000-tons vessel had engines and boilers fitted and was put to sea within the record time of $3\frac{3}{4}$ days after the launch. The world's riveting record was set up on June 5th, 1918, when John Moir drove 11,209 rivets during one normal working day.

The firm can take credit for the fact that during this strenuous war period they played their part in helping to defeat the submarine menace and in making the many units of the Navy entrusted to them efficient in the shortest possible time.

H.M.S. "SQUIRREL"

STERN WHEEL HOSPITAL SHIP

P.60

Three of the many vessels contracted for the Admiralty prior to
and during the Great War.

OUTPUT RECORD—1880 to 1933

AND

PARTICULARS OF VESSELS BUILT—1880 to 1934

OUTPUT 1880-1933

Year	No. of Vessels	Gross Tonnage	I.H.P.
1880	2	800	These vessels not engined by W. C. & Co.
1881	5	1800	
1882	5	6000	
1883	8	8900	
1884	12	9800	
1885	4	7000	
1886	5	8000	
1887	6	3300	
1888	11	10800	
1889	7	18100	
1890	10	15100	
1891	12	21700	
1892	8	22800	8300
1893	9	19000	8100
1894	9	33400	15150
1895	9	34100	19850
1896	12	42900	25000
1897	7	25100	16100
1898	9	53900	31000
1899	7	45500	29950
1900	10	56600	31350
1901	12	53100	33300
1902	12	75800	46900
1903	7	44500	27550
1904	12	44200	34000
1905	12	58000	44250
1906	13	65100	49500
1907	12	60900	45650
1908	8	50600	38400
1909	16	88200	76550
1910	8	50100	36300
1911	10	67600	51800
1912	10	83600	53400
1913	11	84700	60200
1914 1915 1916 1917 1918	77	259850	198850
1919	13	87600	58100
1920	13	80035	55700
1921	13	88558	52250
1922	6	51300	29000
1923	5	40900	26300
1924	9	45800	26550
1925	7	25911	21800
1926	3	26760	15025
1927	6	48911	39450
1928	1	357	450
1929	7	53900	32300
1930	11	54880	48900
1931	3	33300	18200
1932	1	5740	6400
1933	2	13800	12000

PARTICULARS OF VESSELS BUILT 1880-1934

Yard No.	Year	Name	Type	Gross Tonnage	H.P.	Owner
1	1880	"Ethel"	Cargo	265	400	D. Macbrayne
2	,,	"William Hinde"	,,	346	450	William Hinde
3	1881	"Ethelbert"	,,	513	500	Colvils Lowden & Co.
7	1882	"City of Cambridge"	Passenger and Cargo	2576	5800	George Smith & Sons
8	1881	"Ethelwolf"	Cargo	516	500	Colvils Lowden & Co.
9	,,	"Skelligs"	,,	450	400	Clyde Shipping Co.
10	1882	"River Forth"	,,	1127	900	James Little & Co.
11	,,	"Newhaven"	,,	906	600	R. Mackie & Co.
12	,,	"Skerryvore"	Passenger and Cargo	994	1000	Clyde Shipping Co.
13	,,	"Lenore"	Schooner Yacht	102	—	George Smith, Esq.
14	1883	"Teelin Head"	Cargo	1715	1100	Ulster S.S. Co. Ltd.
15	,,	"River Ettrick"	,,	1454	1000	James Little & Co.
16	,,	"Meraggio"	,,	1126	800	Marshall Dodson & Co.
17	,,	"Newington"	,,	1125	500	R. Mackie & Co.
18	,,	"Jane Clark"	,,	838	550	Clark & Service
19	,,	"River Garry"	,,	1339	700	James Little & Co.
20	,,	"Maria A. Hinde"	,,	821	600	William Hinde
21	1884	"Blackwater"	Sailing Ship	538	600	J. McCormick & Co.
22	,,	"Fort George"	Cargo	1756	—	Clark & Service.
23	,,	"Clanrye"	,,	239	280	Newry S. Packet Co.
24	,,	"Corra Linn"	,,	833	550	J. & A. Wyllie.
25	,,	"River Indus"	Passenger and Cargo	3452	1450	James Little & Co.
26	,,	"Alice M. Craig"	Barquentine	387	—	Wm. J. Woodside.
27	,,	"Workman"	,,	387	—	John Atkinson & Co.
28	,,	"Countess of Bantry"	Launch	90	150	Bantry Bay S.S. Co.
29	,,	"Alert"			—	Rangoon Port Commrs.
30	1885	"City of Bombay"	Passenger and Cargo	4491	3700	George Smith & Sons
31	1884	"Carnmoney"	Barque	1299	—	Wm. Porter & Sons
32	,,	"Watchman"	,,	466	—	John Atkinson & Co.
33	,,	"Martha C. Craig"	,,	466	—	W. J. Woodside & Co.
34	,,	"Auric"	Cargo	423	400	H. J. Scott & Co.
35	1885	"Port James"	Sailing Ship	1755	—	Clark & Service
36	1886	"Rosa"	Schooner	67	—	Belfast Harbour Commrs.
37	1885	"Star of Austria"	Sailing	1708	—	Jas. P. Corry & Co.
38	,,	"Polly Woodside"	Schooner	678	—	Wm. J. Woodside
39	1887	"Star of Victoria"	Cargo	3239	1900	Jas. P. Corry & Co.
40	1886	"Elgiva"	,,	667	600	Wm. Porter & Sons
41	,,	"Bessfield"	Barque	1332	—	Wm. Porter & Sons
42	,,	"Ethelbald"	Cargo	657	600	Colvils Lowden & Co.
43	,,	"Broughshane"	,,	325	450	Antrim Iron Ore Co.
44	1897	"Harold"	,,	832	650	Colvils Lowden & Co.
45	,,	"Kathleen"	,,	336	650	John Milligan
46	1888	"Corsican"	,,	338	600	J. & J. MacFarlane
47	,,	—	Dock Caisson		—	British Government
48	,,	—	,,		—	British Government
49	,,	"City of Dublin"	Cargo	3267	1900	George Smith & Sons
50	1887	"Clandeboye"	Paddle Steamer	300	1500	Moore Bros.
51	,,	"Derby Park"	Cargo	1333	—	Colvils Lowden & Co.
52	1888	"Macgregor"	,,	1047	1500	Clark & Service
55	,,	"Fort William"	,,	1807	1000	J. Cuthbertson & Co.
56	,,	"Kirklands"	,,	1807	1000	P. Iredale & Son
57	,,	"Lorton"	Sailing Ship	1419	—	P. Iredale & Son
58	1889	"Star of England"	Cargo Vessel	3511	2200	J. P. Corry & Co.
59	,,	"City of Vienna"	Passenger and Cargo	4672	8700	G. Smith & Sons
60	1888	"Lady Martin"	Ferry	1245	1800	British & Irish Steam Packet Co.
61	,,	"No. 3"	,,		—	Belfast Harbour Commrs.
62	1889	"Hippomenes"	Cargo	2694	1700	R. P. Houston & Co.
63	,,	"Dunmore Head"	,,	2229	3000	Ulster S.S. Co. Ltd.
64	,,	"Iredale"	Sailing Ship	1573	—	P. Iredale & Son
65	,,	"Uranus"	Cargo	1202	1400	Coates & Carver
66	,,	"County Down"	,,	2210	1000	Woodside & Workman
67	1890	"City of Dundee"	,,	3427	4000	G. Smith & Sons
68	,,	"Chichester"	,,	2082	1000	Wm. R. Rea
69	,,	"Nuestra Senora del Carmen"	,,	306	400	Coates & Carver
70	,,	"Marlay"	,,	798	700	R. Tedcastle & Co.

Yard No.	Year	Name	Type	Gross Tonnage	H.P.	Owner
71	1890	"City of Perth"	Cargo	3427	4000	G. Smith & Sons
72	,,	"Ethelwold"	,,	955	1300	Colvils Lowden & Co.
73	,,	"Celtic King"	,,	3737	2000	Wm. Ross & Co.
74	,,	"Helen Craig"	,,	417	540	H. Craig & Co.
75	1891	"Ramore Head"	,,	4444	3300	Ulster S.S. Co. Ltd.
76	1890	"Eveleen"	Ferry	502	700	John Milligan
77	,,	No. 4	,,	—	—	Belfast Harbour Commrs.
78	1891	"Wanderer"	Cargo	4085	3300	T. & J. Harrison
79	,,	"Marian Woodside"	Sailing Ship	1549	—	W. J. Woodside & Co.
80	,,	"Ardanmhor"	Cargo	2081	1200	Clark & Service
81	,,	"Archdale"	Sailing Ship	1557	—	J. H. Iredale & Co.
82	,,	"Rathdown"	,,	2145	—	R. Martin & Co.
83	,,	"M. J. Hedley"	Cargo	442	540	M. J. Hedley S.S. Co.
84	,,	"Lough Neagh"	Barque	973	—	S. McWilliams
85	,,	"Dundonald"	Sailing Ship	2205	—	Thos. Dixon & Sons
86	,,	"Invermore"	,,	1600	—	H. Hutton & Co.
87	1892	"Galgorm Castle"	,,	1596	—	Northern Shiprs. Co. Ltd.
88	1891	"Cave Hill"	,,	2245	—	Belfast Shiprs. Co. Ltd.
89	1891	"Howth"	,,	2244	—	R. Martin & Co.
90	1892	"Crown of Germany"	,,	2241	—	Crown S.S. Co. Ltd.
91	,,	"Southern Cross"	Passenger and Cargo	5050	3200	Wincott Cooper & Co.
93	,,	"Goodrich"	Sailing Ship	2241	—	Boyd Bros. & Co.
94	,,	"Star of New Zealand"	Cargo	4712	2500	J. P. Corry & Co.
95	,,	"Senator"	Sailing Ship	4688	2600	T. & J. Harrison
96	,,	"South African"	,,	438	—	G. W. Philips & Co.
97	,,	"Lauriston"	,,	2301	2300	Galbraith & Moorhead
98	1893	"Ormidale"	Cargo	3360	—	R. & C. Allan
99	,,	"Sophie Kirk"	Barque	958	—	W. J. Woodside & Co.
100	,,	"Jeanie Woodside"	,,	962	—	W. J. Woodside & Co.
101	,,	"Moya"	Cargo	184	—	Commrs. Irish Lights.
102	,,	"Ardanhue"	Tender	2091	600	Clark & Service
103	,,	"Xantippe"	Schooner	972	1600	Montgomerie & Workman
104	,,	"Ardanrose"	Cargo	2123	1600	Clark & Service
105	,,	"Ormiston"	,,	3561	2000	R. & C. Allan
106	,,	"Poltalloch"	Sailing Ship	2254	—	Potter Bros.
107	1894	"Sultan"	Passenger and Cargo	2662	1100	Alfred Holt & Co.
108	,,	"Planet Mercury"	Cargo	3222	1700	R. W. Leyland & Co.
109	,,	"Logician"	,,	4878	2350	T. & J. Harrison
110	,,	"Ching Wa"	Passenger and Cargo	3883	3200	China Mutual S.N. Co. Ltd.
111	1895	"Mount Sirion"	Cargo	3280	1700	Smith & Service
112	,,	"Oopack"	Passenger and Cargo	3384	2200	China Mutual S.N. Co. Ltd.
113	,,	"Urmston Grange"	Cargo	3444	1800	Houlder Bros. & Co. Ltd.
114	,,	"Mourne"	,,	3223	1800	Thos. Dixon & Sons
115	1894	"Sarpedon"	,,	4337	2350	Alfred Holt & Co.
116	,,	"Hector"	,,	4338	2350	Alfred Holt & Co.
118	,,	"Cerberus"	,,	1754	900	Alfred Holt & Co.
119	1895	"Statesman"	,,	6322	3200	T. & J. Harrison
120	,,	"Pakling"	,,	4447	3250	China Mutual S.N. Co. Ltd.
121	,,	"Ardandearg"	,,	3218	1600	Clark & Service
122	,,	"Kintuck"	,,	4447	3250	China Mutual S.N. Co. Ltd.
123	,,	"Hyson"	,,	4445	3250	China Mutual S.N. Co. Ltd.
124	1896	"Langton Grange"	,,	5850	2600	Houlder Bros. & Co.
125	,,	"Denton Grange"	,,	5850	2600	Houlder Bros. & Co.
126	1895	"Centaur"	,,	1900	900	Alfred Holt & Co.
127	,,	"Charon"	,,	1920	900	Alfred Holt & Co.
128	1896	"Patroclus"	,,	5180	3500	Alfred Holt & Co.
129	,,	"Antenor"	,,	5180	3500	Alfred Holt & Co.
130	,,	"Lord Dufferin"	Sailing Ship	2270	—	John Herron & Co.
131	1897	"Glenarm Head"	Cargo	3910	2000	Ulster S.S. Co. Ltd.
132	1896	"Magician"	,,	5065	2350	T. & J. Harrison
133	,,	"City of Sparta"	,,	5179	3600	G. Smith & Sons
134	,,	"Kamakura Maru"	Passenger and Cargo	5813	3300	Nippon Yusen Kaisha
137	,,	"Belvidere"	Passenger and Fruiter	1516	2500	R. & C. Allan
138	1897	"Beverly"	,,	1516	850	R. & C. Allan
139	1896	"Hidalgo"	Cargo	1126	850	New York & Cuba S.S. Co.
140	1897	"Pavia"	,,	2936	1750	Cunard S.S. Co. Ltd.
141	,,	"Tyria"	,,	2936	1750	Cunard S.S. Co. Ltd.
142	,,	"Cypria"	,,	2936	1750	Cunard S.S. Co. Ltd.

Yard No.	Year	Name	Type	Gross Tonnage	H.P.	Owner
143	1898	"Royston Grange"	Cargo	4018	1900	Houlder Bros. & Co.
144	1897	"Sado Maru"	Passenger and Cargo	5900	3300	Nippon Yusen Kaisha
145	1898	"Indore"	Cargo	7300	3750	W. Johnston & Co. Ltd.
146	,,	"Beacon Grange"	Cargo	4018	1900	Houlder Bros. & Co.
147	,,	"City of Corinth"	Passenger and Cargo	5443	3600	G. Smith & Sons
148	,,	"Rippingham Grange"	Cargo	5790	2600	Houlder Bros. & Co.
149	,,	"Workman"	,,	6115	3400	T. & J. Harrison
150	,,	"Castilian"	Passenger and Cargo	7440	4500	J. & A. Allan
151	,,	"Quernmore"	Cargo	7302	4500	Wm. Johnston & Co. Ltd.
152	1899	"Brisgavia"	,,	6575	2800	Hamburg America Line
153	1898	"Heathmore"	,,	3147	1200	Wm. Johnston & Co. Ltd.
154	,,	"Stentor"	,,	6773	3600	Alfred Holt & Co.
155	1899	"Yangtsze"	,,	6457	3235	China Mutual S.N. Co. Ltd.
156	,,	"Ping Suey"	,,	6457	3275	China Mutual S.N. Co. Ltd.
157	,,	"Star of Australia"	,,	7200	3350	J. P. Corry & Co.
158	,,	"Sicilian"	Passenger and Cargo	6010	3350	J. & A. Allan
159	,,	"Lord Downshire"	Cargo	4808	2900	Thos. Dixon & Sons
160	1900	"Corinthian"	Passenger and Cargo	6240	3350	J. & A. Allan
161	1899	"Rathlin Head"	Cargo	6753	3100	Ulster Steamship Co. Ltd.
162	1900	"Mimiro"	,,	6224	2800	Tyser & Co.
166	,,	"Irada"	Passenger and Cargo	8120	5330	Ed. Bates & Son
167	,,	"Calderon"	Cargo	4074	2974	Lamport & Holt
168	,,	"Camoens"	,,	4074	2974	Lamport & Holt.
169	,,	"Mechanician"	,,	9044	3600	T. & J. Harrison
170	,,	"Indian"	Passenger and Cargo	9121	3160	West India & Pacific S.S. Co. Ltd.
171	,,	"City of Athens"	Cargo	5160	2780	Geo. Smith & Sons
172	1901	"Peleus"	,,	7441	3700	Alfred Holt & Co.
173	,,	"Tydeus"	,,	7441	3700	Alfred Holt & Co.
174	1900	"Paknam"	,,	2027	875	Norddeutscher Lloyd
175	,,	"Tanglin"	,,	2027	875	Norddeutscher Lloyd
176	1901	"Carrigan Head"	,,	4201	2360	Ulster S.S. Co. Ltd.
177	,,	"Ionian"	Passenger and Cargo	8265	5100	J. & A. Allan
178	,,	"City of Benares"	,,	6732	4000	Geo. Smith & Sons
180	,,	"City of Madrid"	Cargo	4900	3000	Geo. Smith & Sons
181	,,	"Drayton Grange"	,,	6592	3250	Houlder Bros. & Co.
182	1902	"Oswestry Grange"	,,	6592	3250	Houlder Bros. & Co.
183	1901	"Niwaru"	,,	6450	3250	Tyser & Co.
184	1902	"Telemachus"	,,	7450	3500	Alfred Holt & Co.
185	,,	"Jason"	,,	7450	3500	Alfred Holt & Co.
186	,,	"Lord Antrim"	,,	4270	1750	Thos. Dixon & Sons
187	,,	"Titan"	,,	4170	3150	Lamport & Holt
188	,,	"Tintoretto"	,,	4170	3150	Lamport & Holt
191	,,	"Keemun"	,,	7642	4000	China Mutual S.N. Co. Ltd.
192	,,	"Gregory Apcar"	Passenger and Cargo	4562	3250	Apcar & Co.
193	,,	"Irak"	Cargo	8116	4500	Ed. Bates & Sons
194	,,	"Marere"	,,	6443	3000	Tyser Line Ltd.
195	,,	"Wayfarer"	,,	9600	4000	T. & J. Harrison
197	1903	"City of Calcutta"	Passenger and Cargo	7380	4350	Ellerman Lines Ltd.
198	1902	"Colonial"	Cargo	4955	2700	T. & J. Harrison
199	1903	"Councillor"	,,	4955	2700	T. & J. Harrison
200	,,	"Star of Ireland"	,,	4331	2200	J. P. Corry & Co.
201	,,	"Pars"	,,	7635	3700	P. & O. S.N. Co.
202	,,	"Palma"	,,	7635	3700	P. & O. S.N. Co.
203	,,	"City of Agra"	Passenger and Cargo	4808	2650	Ellerman Lines Ltd.
204	,,	"City of York"	Passenger and Cargo	7705	4800	Ellerman Lines Ltd.
205	1904	"Matatua"	Cargo	6500	4100	Shaw, Savill & Albion Co. Ltd.
206	,,	"Victorian"	Passenger Liner	10630	11000	J. & A. Allan
207	,,	"Parana"	Cargo	3900	2100	Royal Mail S.P. Co. Ltd.
208	,,	No. 6	Ferry	20	25	Belfast Harbour Commrs.
209	,,	"San Jose"	Fruiter	3300	2400	United Fruit Co.
210	,,	"Limon"	,,	3300	2400	United Fruit Co.
211	,,	"Esparta"	,,	3300	2400	United Fruit Co.
212	,,	"Star of Scotland"	Cargo	6230	2850	J. P. Corry & Co.
213	,,	"Telamon"	,,	4510	2200	Alfred Holt & Co.
214	1905	"Anselm"	Passenger and Cargo	5440	4300	Booth Steamship Co. Ltd.
215	1904	"Squirrel," H.M.S.	Coast Guard Cruiser	—	—	Admiralty
216	1905	"City of Karachi"	Passenger and Cargo	5547	3150	Ellerman Lines, Ltd.
217	1904	"Regina"	Cargo	1160	850	R. Truffin & Co., Havana

Yard No.	Year	Name	Type	Gross Tonnage	H.P.	Owner
218	1905	"Delta"	Passenger and Cargo	8053	7000	P. & O. S.N. Co.
219	,,	"Patani"	Cargo	3465	2500	Elder Dempster & Co.
220	,,	"Agberi"	,,	3465	2500	Elder Dempster & Co.
221	,,	"Pacuare"	Fruiter	3891	3150	Elders & Fyffes, Ltd.
222	,,	"Zent"	,,	3891	3150	Elders & Fyffes, Ltd.
223	1904	"Volturnus"	Cargo	160	1600	Alfred Holt & Co.
224	1905	"Orator"	,,	3563	1600	T. & J. Harrison
225	,,	"Bingera"	Passenger and Cargo	2092	3100	Australasian United S.N.Co.Ltd.
226	1906	"City of Glasgow"	,,	6444	4000	Ellerman Lines, Ltd.
227	1905	"Bellerophon"	Cargo	8920	4400	Alfred Holt & Co.
228	,,	"Veronese"	,,	7022	3300	Lamport & Holt
229	,,	"Suva"	Passenger and Cargo	2229	2150	Australasian United S.N.Co.Ltd.
230	1906	"Araguaya"	Passenger Liner	10537	7500	Royal Mail S.P. Co.
231	,,	"Belgravia"	Cargo	6650	2800	Hamburg America Line
232	,,	"Chirripo"	Fruiter	4041	3400	Elders & Fyffes Ltd.
233	,,	"Reventazon"	,,	4041	3400	Elders & Fyffes Ltd.
234	,,	"Japan"	Passenger and Cargo	6013	5000	Apcar & Co.
235	,,	"Star of Japan"	Cargo	6236	3000	J. P. Corry & Co.
236	,,	"City of London"	Passenger and Cargo	8875	6500	Ellerman Lines Ltd.
237	,,	"Howth Head"	Cargo	4440	2400	Ulster S.S. Co. Ltd.
238	,,	"Salaga"	,,	3810	2650	Elder Dempster & Co.
239	,,	"Gando"	,,	3810	2650	Elder Dempster & Co.
240	,,	"Chyebassa"	,,	6250	4250	British India S.N. Co. Ltd.
241	1907	"Ceara"	Passenger and Cargo	3324	2700	Lloyd Brazileiro
242	,,	"Para"	,,	3324	2700	Lloyd Brazileiro
245	,,	"São Paulo"	,,	3583	2600	Lloyd Brazileiro
246	,,	"Rio de Janeiro"	,,	3583	2600	Lloyd Brazileiro
247	,,	"Whakarua"	Cargo	6600	3500	Tyser Line Ltd.
248	,,	"Nerehana"	,,	6600	3500	Tyser Line Ltd.
255	,,	"Kia Ora"	Passenger and Cargo	6560	4100	Shaw Savill & Albion Co. Ltd.
256	,,	"Verdi"	,,	6580	3850	Lamport & Holt
263	1909	"Bahia"	,,	3401	2700	Lloyd Brazileiro
264	,,	"Minas Geraea"	,,	3401	2700	Lloyd Brazileiro
265	1907	"Coppename"	Passenger and Fruiter	3192	2500	Koninklijke West-Indische Maildienst
266	1908	"Marowijne"	,,	3192	2500	Koninklijke West-Indische Maildienst
267	1907	"Mantiqueira"	Cargo	1696	1000	Lloyd Brazileiro
268	1909	"Bocaina"	,,	1696	1000	Lloyd Brazileiro
269	,,	"Pyrineus"	,,	1696	1000	Lloyd Brazileiro
270	1907	"Ancona"	Passenger and Cargo	8210	5300	Societa di Navigazio a Vapore Italia
271	1908	"Verona"	,,	8210	5300	Societa di Navigazio a Vapore Italia
272	,,	"Cartago"	Passenger and Fruiter	4940	3000	United Fruit Co.
273	,,	"Parismina"	,,	4940	3000	United Fruit Co.
274	,,	"Heredia"	,,	4940	3000	United Fruit Co.
275	,,	"Perseus"	Cargo	6728	4200	Alfred Holt & Co.
276	,,	"Theseus"	,,	6728	4200	Alfred Holt & Co.
277	,,	"Taimui"	Passenger and Cargo	9957	5000	Shaw Savill & Albion Co. Ltd.
278	1909	"Otranto"	Passenger Liner	12124	10000	Orient Steam Nav. Co. Ltd.
279	,,	"Orvieto"	,,	12124	10000	Orient Steam Nav. Co. Ltd.
280	,,	"Abangarez"	Passenger and Fruiter	4960	3000	United Fruit Co.
281	,,	"Turrialba"	,,	4960	3000	United Fruit Co.
282	,,	"Atenas"	,,	4960	3000	United Fruit Co.
283	,,	"Star of Canada"	Cargo	7280	4000	J. P. Corry & Co.
284	,,	"Almirante"	Passenger and Fruiter	5010	3000	United Fruit Co.
285	,,	"Sante Marta"	,,	5010	3000	United Fruit Co.
286	,,	"Metapan"	,,	5010	3000	United Fruit Co.
287	,,	"Zacapa"	,,	5010	3000	United Fruit Co.
288	,,	"Professor"	Cargo	3580	1600	T. & J. Harrison
289	,,	"Rangatira"	,,	7465	4550	Shaw Savill & Albion Co. Ltd.
290	1910	"Tenet"	,,	606	1600	W. A. Grainger
291	,,	"Muritai"	,,	7280	4000	Tyser & Co.
292	,,	"St. Albans"	Passenger and Cargo	4120	3050	Eastern and Australian S.S. Co. Ltd.
293	,,	"Kansas"	Cargo	6074	3050	Bucknall S.S. Co.
294	,,	"Aeneas"	Passenger Liner	10050	5400	Alfred Holt & Co.
295	,,	"Ascanius"	,,	10050	5400	Alfred Holt & Co.
296	1911	"Anchises"	,,	10050	5400	Alfred Holt & Co.
297	1910	"Star of India"	Cargo	7316	4000	J. P. Corry & Co.

Yard No.	Year	Name	Type	Gross Tonnage	H.P.	Owner
298	1910	"Arankola" ..	Passenger and Cargo ..	4026	5500	British India S.N. Co. Ltd.
299	1911	"Neleus" ..	Cargo	6686	4200	Alfred Holt & Co.
300	,,	Aracataca ..	Passenger and Fruiter	4154	3400	Elders & Fyffes Ltd.
301	1912	"Van 'yck" ..	Passenger Liner ..	9862	6200	Lamport & Holt
302	,,	"Vauban" ..	,, ,, ..	9862	6200	Lamport & Holt
303	,,	"Vestris" ..	,, ,, ..	9862	6200	Lamport & Holt.
304	1911	"Tivives" ..	Passenger and Fruiter	5017	3000	United Fruit Co.
305	,,	"Carrillo" ..	,, ,,	5017	3000	United Fruit Co.
306	,,	"Sixaola" ..	,, ,,	5017	3000	United Fruit Co.
307	,,	"Egra" ..	Passenger and Cargo	5108	6250	British India S.N. Co. Ltd.
308	,,	"Ekma" ..	,, ,,	5108	6250	British India S.N. Co. Ltd.
309	,,	"Waimana" ..	,, ,,	10390	4700	Shaw Savill & Albion Co. Ltd.
310	1912	"Makarini" ..	Cargo	10624	4300	Tyser & Co.
311	,,	"Demodocus" ..	,, ...	6700	4200	Alfred Holt & Co.
312	,,	"Laomedon" ..	,, ...	6700	4200	Alfred Holt & Co.
313	,,	"Hawkes Bay" ..	,, ...	10624	4300	Tyser & Co.
314	1913	"Pastores" ..	Passenger and Fruiter	7782	6100	United Fruit Co.
315	,,	"Tenadores" ..	,, ,,	7782	6100	United Fruit Co.
316	,,	"Calamares" ..	,, ,,	7782	6100	United Fruit Co.
317	1912	"Patia" ..	,, ,,	6103	4300	Elders & Fyffes Ltd.
318	1913	"Nestor" ..	Passenger Liner ..	14500	7600	Alfred Holt & Co.
319	,,	"Ulysses" ..	,, ,,	14500	7600	Alfred Holt & Co.
320	,,	"Patuca" ..	Passenger and Fruiter	6103	4300	Elders & Fyffes Ltd.
321	,,	"Eumaeus" ..	Cargo	6700	4200	Alfred Holt & Co.
322	,,	"Phemius" ..	,, ...	6700	4200	Alfred Holt & Co.
323	1912	"Kentucky" ..	,, ...	6590	3300	Bucknall S.S. Lines
324	1913	"Cardiganshire" ..	,, ...	9426	5000	Royal Mail S.P. Co.
325	,,	"Carnarvonshire" ..	,, ...	9426	5000	Royal Mail S.P. Co.
326	1918	"Dunaff Head" ..	,, ...	5258	3100	Ulster S.S. Co. Ltd.
327	1918	"Melmore Head" ..	,, ...	5320	3100	Ulster S.S. Co. Ltd.
328	1913	"Port Melbourne" ..	,, ...	9152	5000	J. P. Corry & Co.
329	1914	"Port Sydney" ..	Passenger and Cargo	9152	5200	J. P. Corry & Co.
330	,,	"City of Exeter" ..	,, ,,	9373	5200	Ellerman Lines, Ltd.
331	,,	"City of Nagpur" ..	,, ,,	8331	4550	Ellerman Lines, Ltd.
332	,,	"City of Vienna" ..	Cargo	6111	3100	Ellerman Lines, Ltd.
333	,,	"Ebro" ..	Passenger Liner ..	8463	5800	Pacific Steam Nav. Co.
334	,,	"Essequibo" ..	,, ,,	8463	5800	Pacific Steam Nav. Co.
335	,,	"Pyrrhus" ..	Cargo	7603	4700	Alfred Holt & Co.
336	,,	"Carmarthenshire" ..	Passenger and Cargo	7823	3750	Royal Mail S.P. Co.
337	,,	"Pembrokeshire" ..	,, ,,	7823	3750	Royal Mail S.P. Co.
338	1915	"Cavina" ..	Passenger and Fruiter	6539	4800	Elders & Fyffes, Ltd.
339	,,	"Coronada" ..	,, ,,	6539	4800	Elders & Fyffes, Ltd.
340	1917	"Ulua" ..	,, ,,	7452	4900	United Fruit Co.
341	,,	"Toloa" ..	,, ,,	7452	4900	United Fruit Co.
342	1915	"San Mateo" ..	Fruiter	3301	2300	United Fruit Co.
343	,,	"San Pablo" ..	,, ...	3301	2300	United Fruit Co.
344	,,	"San Rito" ..	,, ...	3301	2300	United Fruit Co.
345	1918	"San Andres" ..	,, ...	3301	2300	United Fruit Co.
346	1915	"Tela" ..	Passenger and Fruiter	7226	4900	United Fruit Co.
347	1920	"San Blas" ..	Fruiter	3628	2500	United Fruit Co.
348	1920	"San Bruno" ..	,, ...	3627	2500	United Fruit Co.
349	1917	"Mahana" ..	Cargo	11800	6000	Shaw Savill & Albion Co. Ltd.
350	,,	"Mahia" ..	,, ...	10800	4700	Shaw Savill & Albion Co. Ltd.
351	,,	"Port Darwin" ..	,, ...	10365	4400	Commonwealth & Dominion Line, Ltd.
352	,,	"Port Denison" ..	,, ...	10365	4400	Commonwealth & Dominion Line, Ltd.
353	,,	"Fanad Head" ..	,, ...	5200	2600	Ulster, S.S. Co.
354	,,	"Munardan" ..	,, ...	3813	2500	Clark & Service
355	1920	"City of Cambridge" ..	,, ...	7055	3400	Ellerman Lines, Ltd.
356	1918	"Port Bowen" ..	,, ...	8267	6100	Commonwealth & Dominion Line Ltd.
357	1921	"Calchas" ..	,, ...	10304	8000	Alfred Holt & Co.
358	1919	"Port Caroline" ..	,, ...	8267	6500	Commonwealth & Dominion Line Ltd.
359	1921	"Vandyck" ..	Passenger Liner ..	13233	8500	Lamport & Holt
360	1923	"Voltaire" ..	,, ,,	13233	8500	Lamport & Holt
361	1916	"P.15", H.M.S.	Patrol Boat ..	470	4000	Admiralty
362	1916	"P.16", H.M.S.	,, ,, ..	470	4000	Admiralty
363	1915	"P.17", H.M.S.	,, ,, ..	470	4000	Admiralty
364	1920	"San Gil" ..	Fruiter	3628	2500	United Fruit Co.

Yard No.	Year	Name	Type	Gross Tonnage	H.P.	Owner
365	1919	"Chirripo"	Passenger and Fruiter	5360	4100	Elders & Fyffes
366	1916	"Pentstemon" H.M.S.	Sloop	930	2200	Admiralty
367	1916	"Petunia" H.M.S.	—	930	2200	Admiralty
368	,,	"Apple Leaf"	Oil Tanker	5900	6000	Admiralty
369	1921	"Reventazon"	Passenger and Fruiter	5360	4100	Admiralty
377	1916	—	Steam Launch	—	—	Admiralty
378	,,	—	—	—	—	Admiralty
379	1921	"Orania"	Passenger Liner	9771	7000	Koninklijke H. Lloyd
380	1917	"P.60" H.M.S.	Patrol Boat	—	—	Admiralty
381	,,	"P.61" H.M.S.	—	—	—	Admiralty
382	1922	"Port Auckland"	Cargo	8308	4500	Commonwealth & Dominion Line Ltd.
383	,,	"Port Campbell"	,,	8308	4500	Commonwealth & Dominion Line Ltd.
388	1917	—	Sternwheel Hospital Vessel	—	—	Admiralty
389	,,	—	,,	—	—	Admiralty
390	,,	—	,,	—	—	Admiralty
391	,,	—	,,	—	—	Admiralty
392	1922	"Diomed"	Cargo	10340	8000	Alfred Holt & Co.
393	1923	"Torr Head"	,,	5221	2800	Ulster S.S. Co. Ltd.
400	1918	"P.C.69" H.M.S.	Patrol Boat	—	—	Admiralty
401	1917	"P.C.70" H.M.S.	,,	—	—	Admiralty
402	1917	"Syringa," H.M.S.	Sloop	1123	2850	Admiralty
403	1918	"Windflower" H.M.S.	,,	1123	2850	Admiralty
414	1917	"B.V.1"	Boom Defence Vessel	—	—	Admiralty
415	,,	"B.V.2"	,,	—	—	Admiralty
416	,,	"B.V.3"	,,	—	—	Admiralty
417	,,	"B.V.4"	,,	—	—	Admiralty
418	,,	"B.V.5"	,,	—	—	Admiralty
419	,,	"B.V.6"	,,	—	—	Admiralty
420	,,	"B.V.7"	,,	—	—	Admiralty
421	,,	"B.V.8"	,,	—	—	Admiralty
422	,,	"B.V.9"	,,	—	—	Admiralty
423	,,	"B.V.10"	,,	—	—	Admiralty
424	1918	"British Lantern"	Oil Tanker	6897	3200	British Tanker Co. Ltd.
425	,,	"British Beacon"	,,	6897	3200	British Tanker Co. Ltd.
426	,,	"War Beetle"	Cargo	5177	2800	Shipping Controller
427	,,	"War Leopard"	,,	5177	2800	Shipping Controller
428	,,	"B.D.31"	Boom Defence Vessel	—	—	Admiralty
429	,,	"B.D.32"	,,	—	—	Admiralty
430	,,	"B.D.33"	,,	—	—	Admiralty
431	,,	"B.D.34"	,,	—	—	Admiralty
432	,,	"B.D.35"	,,	—	—	Admiralty
433	,,	"B.D.36"	,,	—	—	Admiralty
436	,,	"War Argus"	Cargo	7910	5800	Shipping Controller
437	1919	"Nowshera"	,,	7920	5800	British India S.N. Co.
438	1918	"Royal tar"	,,	7900	5800	Blue Star Line
439	1919	"Albionstar"	,,	7900	5800	Blue Star Line
440	,,	"Wangaratta"	,,	7920	5800	British India S.N. Co.
441	,,	"Muneric"	,,	5146	2800	Clark & Service
442	,,	"Ballygally Head"	,,	5180	2800	Ulster S.S. Co. Ltd.
443	,,	"Gogra"	,,	5181	2800	British India S.N. Co.
444	,,	"Gorala"	,,	5181	2800	British India S.N. Co.
445	,,	"Kenbane Head"	,,	5180	2800	Ulster S.S. Co. Ltd.
446	,,	"Narenta"	,,	8266	4500	Royal Mail S.P. Co.
447	,,	"Port Curtis"	,,	8287	4500	Commonwealth & Dominion Line Ltd.
448	1920	"Nebraska"	Cargo	8266	4500	Royal Mail S.P. Co.
449	,,	"Canonesa"	,,	8286	4500	Furness-Houlder Argentine Lines Ltd.
450	1921	"Nictheroy"	Sugar Vessel	8266	4500	Royal Mail S.P. Co. Ltd.
454	,,	"Mayari"	,,	2802	1500	United Fruit Co.
455	,,	"Macabi"	,,	2802	1500	United Fruit Co.
456	,,	"Manaqui"	,,	2802	1500	United Fruit Co.
457	,,	"Maravi"	,,	2802	1500	United Fruit Co.
459	,,	"San Benito"	Passenger and Fruiter	3724	3100	United Fruit Co.
460	1923	"Dardanus"	Cargo	7857	7000	Alfred Holt & Co.

Yard No.	Year	Name	Type	Gross Tonnage	H.P.	Owner
462	1923	"Port Brisbane"	Cargo	8315	4500	Commonwealth & Dominion Line Ltd.
463	1924	"Port Wellington"	,,	7868	4500	Commonwealth & Dominion Line Ltd.
464	1922	"City of Nagpur"	Passenger Liner	10140	5750	Ellerman Lines, Ltd.
465	,,	"British Workman"	Oil Tanker	6993	4000	British Tanker Co.
466	,,	"British Engineer"	,,	6993	4000	British Tanker Co.
467	1923	"Berwindmoor"	Topside Tank Collier	6078	2800	Berwindmoor S.S. Co.
468	1924	"City of Venice"	Passenger and Cargo	8308	4300	Ellerman Lines Ltd.
469	,,	"Arlington Court"	Cargo	4915	1650	Haldin & Co.
470	,,	"Barrington Court"	,,	4915	1650	Haldin & Co.
471	,,	"Marudu"	Passenger Vessel	1926	2000	Alfred Holt & Co.
472	,,	"Atlantida"	Passenger and Fruiter	4191	4000	Standard Fruit & S.S. Co.
473	,,	"Buchanness"	Cargo	4573	1800	Sir Wm. Reardon Smith and Sons, Ltd.
474	,,	"Skegness"	,,	4573	1800	Sir Wm. Reardon Smith and Sons, Ltd.
475	,,	"Antinous"	,,	4563	1800	J. Langdon Rees, Ltd.
476	1925	"Errington Court"	,,	4915	1650	Haldin & Co.
477	,,	"Port Dunedin"	Passenger and Cargo	7463	5500	Commonwealth & Dominion Line Ltd.
481	,,	"Federiko Glavic"	Cargo	5269	2200	Dubrovacka Parobrodska Plovidba
484	,,	"Jevington Court"	Passenger and Fruiter	4544	1650	Haldin & Co.
485	,,	"Gatun"	,,	3362	3000	Standard Fruit & S.S. Co.
486	1926	"Orestes"	Cargo	7882	8000	Alfred Holt & Co.
487	,,	"Idomeneus"	,,	7882	8000	Alfred Holt & Co.
488	,,	"Llandaff Castle"	Passenger Vessel	10786	5800	Union Castle Mail S.S. Co.Ltd.
489	1927	"Port Freemantle"	Passenger and Cargo	8072	6800	Commonwealth & Dominion Line Ltd.
490	,,	"Bermuda"	Passenger Liner	20000	15000	Bermuda and West Indies Steamship Co. Ltd.
491	,,	"Tela"	Passenger and Fruiter	4083	4000	United Fruit Co.
492	,,	"Castilla"	,,	4083	4000	United Fruit Co.
493	,,	"Iriona"	,,	4083	4000	United Fruit Co.
494	1928	"Chesapeake"	Oil Tanker	8955	4600	Anglo American Oil Co.
502	,,	"Divis"	Sludge Vessel	360	450	Belfast City Corp.
503	1929	"Agamemnon"	Cargo	7886	10000	Alfred Holt & Co.
504	,,	"City of Sydney"	,,	6986	5200	Ellerman Lines, Ltd.
505	,,	"Kosmos"	Whaling Factory	17800	4800	Hvalfangerselskapet Kosmos A/S (Anders Jahre)
506	,,	"Deebank"	Cargo	5060	2600	Andrew Weir & Co.
507	,,	"Trentbank"	,,	5060	2600	Andrew Weir & Co.
508	,,	"Forthbank"	,,	5060	2600	Andrew Weir & Co.
509	,,	"Lindenbank"	,,	5060	2600	Andrew Weir & Co.
510	1930	"Irisbank"	,,	5627	6000	Andrew Weir & Co.
511	,,	"Lossiebank"	,,	5627	6000	Andrew Weir & Co.
512	,,	"Taybank"	,,	5627	6000	Andrew Weir & Co.
513	,,	"Tweedbank"	,,	5627	6000	Andrew Weir & Co.
514	,,	"Cefalu"	Passenger and Fruiter	5222	4500	Standard Fruit & S.S. Co.
515	,,	"Musa"	,,	5833	7850	United Fruit Co.
516	,,	"Corabank"	Oil Tanker	8898	3000	Andrew Weir & Co.
517	,,	"William Strachan"	,,	6157	3000	Oppen & Sorensen's Tankrederi A/S
518	1931	"Conus"	,,	8132	5400	Anglo Saxon Petroleum Co.
519	,,	"Corbis"	,,	8132	5400	Anglo Saxon Petroleum Co.
520	1930	"Mavis"	Cargo	935	950	General Steam Nav. Co.
521	,,	"Swift"	,,	936	950	General Steam Nav. Co.
522	1931	"Kosmos II"	Whaling Factory	16966	5400	Hvalfangerselskapet Kosmos II A/S (Anders Jahre)
524	1932	"Erin"	Passenger and Fruiter	5739	6400	Standard Fruit & S.S. Co.
530	1933	"Isipingo"	Passenger and Cargo	6900	6000	Andrew Weir & Co.
531	,,	"Inchanga"	,,	6900	6000	Andrew Weir & Co.
*532	1934	"Incomati"	,,	7000	6000	Andrew Weir & Co.
*533	,,	"Durham"	Cargo	11000	12500	New Zealand Shipping Co.
*534	,,	"Dorset"	,,	11000	12500	New Zealand Shipping Co.
*535	1935	"Acarus"	Tanker	8010	4640	Anglo Saxon Petroleum Co.

Dumb Barges and other small craft not included in this output list.

* *Information added 2004 by Dr. John Lynch*

MARCONI
WIRELESS INSTALLATIONS
1900 - 1933

THE two world-renowned firms of Messrs. Workman Clark, Shipbuilders, of Belfast, and the Marconi International Marine Communication Co., Ltd. have worked in the closest co-operation for nearly a quarter of a century.

Marconi wireless apparatus of all types has been fitted on ships built in this famous Belfast Yard from the time, 25 years ago, when spark transmitters and magnetic detector receivers with limited ranges were the last word in wireless equipment for ships.

To-day ships built by Messrs. Workman Clark carry the very latest designs of Marconi valve transmitters and receivers with world-wide ranges.

In these instances two essential conditions for good voyaging have been met—a well-found ship and the most reliable wireless equipment in the world.

THE MARCONI INTERNATIONAL MARINE COMMUNICATION CO., LTD.
MARCONI OFFICES : Electra House, Victoria Embankment, LONDON, W.C.2

Telephone : TEMPLE BAR 4321. : : : : Telegrams : "THULIUM, ESTRAND, LONDON."

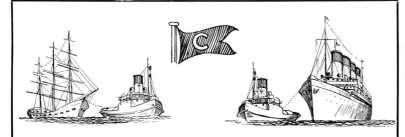

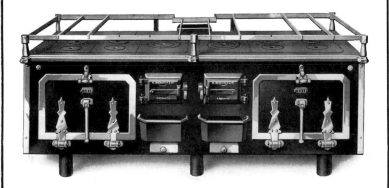

LIFEBOATS

TO BOARD OF TRADE REQUIREMENTS

YACHTS, LAUNCHES
SKIFFS, DINGHIES, BARGES

BUILT AND FITTED COMPLETE

◇

ENQUIRIES INVITED FOR REPAIRS, RENEWALS
AND CONVERSIONS TO HULL OR MACHINERY
FOR ALL DESCRIPTIONS OF SMALL CRAFT

FLOATING DOCK UP TO 60' 0"

◇

MASTS, YARDS, DERRICKS

GREGSON & Cº Lᵀᴰ.

SILVOCEA WHARF, LEAMOUTH RD., LONDON, E.14
TELEPHONE: EAST 0971.

[xxvii]

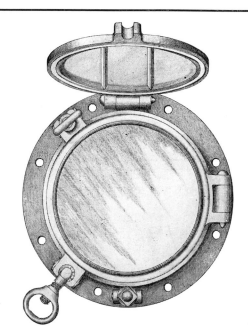
7

[xxxii]

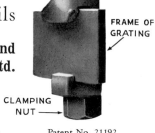
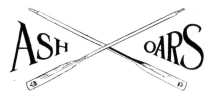

INDEX TO ADVERTISERS